Behavioral Sciences

Behavioral Sciences

PreTest® Self-Assessment and Review

Fourth Edition

Edited by

Evan G. Pattishall, Jr., Ph.D., M.D.
Research Professor of Behavioral Science, Health and Human
  Development
College of Health and Human Development
The Pennsylvania State University
University Park, Pennsylvania

McGraw-Hill Book Company
Health Professions Division
PreTest Series

Colorado Springs   New York
Oklahoma City   St. Louis   San Francisco
Auckland   Bogotá   Caracas   Hamburg
Lisbon   London   Madrid   Mexico   Milan
Montreal   New Delhi   Panama   Paris
San Juan   São Paulo   Singapore   Sydney
Tokyo   Toronto

Library of Congress Cataloging-in-Publication Data

Behavioral sciences.

  Bibliography: p.
  1. Psychology—Examinations, questions, etc.
2. Social sciences—Examinations, questions, etc.
I. Pattishall, Evan G. (Evan Gradick), 1921–
[DNLM: 1. Behavior—examination questions.
2. Behavioral Sciences—examination questions.
WM 18 B419]
BF78.B43   1988   150'.76   87-25982
ISBN 0-07-051962-5

This book was set in Times Roman by Waldman Graphics, Inc.; the editors were J. Dereck Jeffers and Bruce MacGregor; the production supervisor was Clara B. Stanley.
Semline, Inc., was printer and binder.

1234567890 SEMSEM 894321098

ISBN 0-07-051962-5

Contents

Introduction

Behavioral Sciences, PreTest® Self-Assessment and Review has been designed to provide students, as well as physicians, with a comprehensive and convenient instrument for self-assessment and review within the field of behavioral sciences. The 500 questions provided have the same format and are of the same degree of difficulty as the questions contained in Part I of the National Board of Medical Examiners examinations, the Federation Licensing Examination (FLEX), and the Foreign Medical Graduate Examination in the Medical Sciences (FMGEMS).

Each question in the book is accompanied by an answer, an explanation, and specific page references to current journal articles, textbooks, or both. A bibliography, listing all the sources used in the book, follows the last chapter.

Perhaps the most effective way to use this book is to allow yourself one minute to answer each question in a given chapter; as you proceed, indicate your answer beside each question. By following this suggestion, you will be approximating the time limits imposed by the board examinations previously mentioned.

When you finish answering the questions in a chapter, you should then spend as much time as you need verifying your answers and carefully reading the explanations. Although you should pay special attention to the explanations for the questions you answered incorrectly, you should read every explanation. The authors of this book have designed the explanations to reinforce and supplement the information tested by the questions. If, after reading the explanations for a given chapter, you feel you need still more information about the material covered, you should consult and study the references indicated.

Behavioral Sciences

Biological Correlates and Behavioral Medicine

DIRECTIONS: Each question below contains five suggested responses. Select the **one best** response to each question.

1. All the following endocrine glands are subject to control by the brain EXCEPT the _(by blood level of Ca)_

(A) pancreatic islets
(B) pituitary
(C) parathyroid
(D) thyroid
(E) adrenal

2. All the following hormones are recognized as being important in the control of sexual behavior EXCEPT

(A) luteinizing hormone releasing factor
(B) oxytocin
(C) estradiol
(D) testosterone
(E) androstenedione

3. Siblings of schizophrenics are more likely to become schizophrenic than are persons chosen randomly from the population by a factor of about

(A) 2
(B) 4
(C) 6
(D) 8
(E) 10

4. The most important (frequent) genetic cause of mental retardation is

(A) Bartholin-Patau syndrome
(B) Edwards' syndrome
(C) Down's syndrome
(D) Turner's syndrome
(E) Klinefelter's syndrome

5. When an axon is cut, all the following events take place EXCEPT

(A) there is a rapid local degeneration of the axon and myelin sheath
(B) macrophages from the general circulation are unable to enter the area to phagocytose axonal debris
(C) proliferation of fibrous astrocytes forms a glial scar around the zone of trauma
(D) scarring can block the course taken by the regenerating axons
(E) degeneration spreads in both directions along the axon from the zone of trauma

1

6. All the following are basic principles of the neural basis of learning and memory EXCEPT

(A) memory has stages and is continually changing
(B) long-term memory results in physical changes in the brain
(C) memory traces are widely distributed throughout the nervous system
(D) the hippocampus and temporal lobes are most actively involved in the human memory process
(E) trauma can completely destroy stored memory

7. Clinical features of major depressive disorders suggest a defect in the

(A) frontal lobes
(B) pituitary
(C) hippocampus
(D) hypothalamus
(E) corpus callosum

8. All the following statements on the influence of environment on brain structure and behavior are true EXCEPT that

(A) the structure of the brain is to an important degree specified by genetic and developmental processes
(B) the pattern of interconnections between neurons is influenced considerably by experience
(C) there is very little evidence for the notion of the critical period in the development of normal social and perceptual competence
(D) at certain critical stages in its development, the integrative action of the brain and its cellular structure are dependent upon its interaction with its environment
(E) the action of the environment on the brain varies with age

9. Ethology has made major contributions to understanding human behavior through all the following concepts EXCEPT

(A) fixed action pattern
(B) critical period
(C) imprinting
(D) ethnic bonds
(E) "sign-stimulus"

10. Prefrontal lobotomy to reduce anxiety has fallen into disfavor because of all the following side effects EXCEPT

(A) lack of inhibition
(B) reduction in intellectual capability
(C) development of epilepsy
(D) abnormal personality changes
(E) reduction of initiative and drive

11. A person with Klinefelter's syndrome has the genotype

(A) XY
(B) YY
(C) XXY
(D) XYY
(E) XXX

12. Heredity accounts for approximately what percentage of total variation in IQ scores within a family?

(A) 5 percent
(B) 25 percent
(C) 50 percent
(D) 75 percent
(E) 100 percent

13. The complex of severe psychologic disorders known as schizophrenia has a demonstrable basis that is characterized as

(A) environmentally determined
(B) polygenic
(C) a chromosomal aberration
(D) a simple recessive trait
(E) an inborn error of metabolism

14. A disorder resulting from a single gene defect that may produce severe mental problems is

(A) manic-depressive psychosis
(B) dyslexia
(C) phenylketonuria
(D) Porter's syndrome
(E) Down's syndrome

15. All the following statements concerning the mechanisms of the development of coronary heart disease are currently held to be true EXCEPT that

(A) repeated excessive heart rate or pressor responses to behavioral stressors can promote arterial injury through turbulence and sheer stress
(B) increased output of catecholamines and corticosteroids is biochemically toxic to coronary arteries
(C) increased circulating catecholamines influence platelet aggregation and the mobilization of serum lipids
(D) acute behavioral stressors can raise thresholds for ventricular fibrillation
(E) disruption of central nervous system control of the heart can initiate arrhythmic activity

16. Behavioral medicine has demonstrated significant contributions to the treatment of all the following diseases or conditions EXCEPT *(neural control of heart rate is not possible in heart block.)*

(A) hypertension
(B) cardiac arrhythmias
(C) Raynaud's disease
(D) third-degree heart block
(E) asthma

relaxation technique

17. The pituitary secretion of endorphins is closely linked to the secretion of adrenocorticotropic hormone (ACTH) so that endorphins facilitate the ability to respond to

(A) retarded growth
(B) severe hypertension
(C) stress
(D) chronic pain
(E) tachycardia

18. Psychosocial stress affects catecholamine secretion to induce an increase of all the following cardiovascular pathogenic phenomena EXCEPT

(A) rate of damage to intima of coronary arteries
(B) blood pressure and heart rate
(C) blood lipids
(D) first degree AV block
(E) ventricular arrhythmias

19. Minor tranquilizers are preferable to barbiturates in treating neuroses for all the following reasons EXCEPT

(A) there is less risk of overdose
(B) tolerance is not as easily developed
(C) there is greater efficacy with anxious patients
(D) dependence is not as strong
(E) evidence of dependence is more readily established

20. Hyperventilation from anxiety, threat, or fear results in all the following EXCEPT

(A) reduced CO_2 in the blood
(B) reduced blood acid level
(C) increased sympathetic activity
(D) increased risk of cardiac arrhythmia
(E) increased oxygen supplied to brain tissue

21. Dream deprivation in humans tends to produce

(A) impaired performance on simple verbal tasks with no emotional content
(B) less total need for dream sleep
(C) major impairment of psychological functions
(D) retardation of memory formation
(E) integration of emotional material with memories of other experiences

22. In obese persons, food intake is

(A) controlled more by physiological state than by external cues
(B) high because these individuals have difficulty metabolizing food
(C) likely to result in excessive consumption of bad-tasting food
(D) regulated in a fashion similar to that of rats with ventromedial hypothalamic lesions
(E) the result of a willingness to expend more effort to get food than is exhibited by nonobese persons

23. Experimental behavioral stress-conditioning procedures can induce significant increases in all the following EXCEPT

(A) plasma potassium
(B) plasma sodium
(C) plasma aldosterone
(D) blood pressure
(E) heart rate

24. When individuals with type A coronary-prone behavior patterns are subjected to stressful situations, they exhibit increases in all the following physiological responses EXCEPT

(A) plasma norepinephrine levels
(B) systolic blood pressure
(C) heart rate
(D) occipital alpha activity
(E) cortisol levels

25. Over time, vigorous exercise results in all the following EXCEPT

(A) increased high-density lipoprotein cholesterol (HDL-C)
(B) decreased low-density lipoprotein cholesterol (LDL-C)
(C) decreased very low-density lipoprotein cholesterol (VLDL-C)
(D) decreased total cholesterol
(E) increased triglycerides

26. Harry Harlow's work with inanimate surrogate mothers for monkeys suggests that the early experience critical to the ultimate development of "love" is

(A) positive reinforcement
(B) protection from danger
(C) contact comfort
(D) need-reduction by nursing
(E) sexual stimulation

27. The hormone best known for its role in aggression is

(A) thyroxine
(B) testosterone
(C) estrogen
(D) progesterone
(E) aldosterone

28. A direct pathological consequence of stress-induced plasma cortisone elevation is injury to the

(A) neuroendocrine system
(B) immune system
(C) cardiovascular musculature
(D) hypothalamus
(E) central nervous system

29. The severe deterioration in psychological and motor functioning associated with general paresis is a result of

(A) chromosomal abnormalities
(B) cerebral anoxia at birth
(C) infection of the brain by spirochetes
(D) extrapyramidal complications of thorazine treatment
(E) high intake of opiate derivatives

30. All the following statements about Down's syndrome are true EXCEPT that

(A) most affected persons have 47 chromosomes
(B) the incidence of Down's syndrome is related to maternal age
(C) amniocentesis can detect the presence of Down's syndrome before birth
(D) it accounts for approximately 30 percent of retarded children in the United States
(E) most infants born with Down's syndrome die at an early age

31. The gate control theory of pain assumes all the following EXCEPT that

(A) the substantia gelatinosa is the primary vehicle for gating
(B) the spinal gate mechanism is influenced by nerve impulses that descend from the brain
(C) the activity in the large nerve fibers will tend to facilitate the transmission by opening the gate
(D) motivation, emotion, and cognition modulate the pain experience
(E) the spinal gate mechanism in the dorsal horn modulates the transmission from afferent fibers to spinal cord transmission cells

32. The most effective behavioral medicine treatment for migraine headache has been found to be

(A) psychotherapy
(B) hypnosis
(C) finger temperature biofeedback
(D) alpha EEG biofeedback
(E) frontalis EMG biofeedback

33. All the following are risk factors of cardiovascular disease EXCEPT

(A) physical inactivity
(B) cigarette smoking
(C) obesity
(D) personality behavior type
(E) moderate alcohol consumption

DIRECTIONS: Each question below contains four suggested responses of which **one or more** is correct. Select

A	if	**1, 2, and 3**	are correct
B	if	**1 and 3**	are correct
C	if	**2 and 4**	are correct
D	if	**4**	is correct
E	if	**1, 2, 3, and 4**	are correct

34. The prominence of genetic factors in alcoholism is illustrated by which of the following?

(1) Close relatives of alcoholics have a fourfold increased risk
(2) An alcoholic's children who are given up for adoption at birth are at fourfold increased risk
(3) The risk for the identical twin of an alcoholic is about 60 percent
(4) Close relatives of alcoholics are significantly more vulnerable for other psychiatric illnesses

35. Factors that have potential influence on a person's gender identity include

(1) chromosomal configuration (XX or XY)
(2) gender assigned at birth
(3) internal reproductive structures
(4) response of parent to child's assigned gender

36. Studies of the effects of acute and chronic stress in humans indicate that affected components of the immune system include which of the following?

(1) Polymorphonuclear granulocytes
(2) Lymphocyte T-cell cytotoxic action
(3) Production of interferon
(4) Natural killer-cell activity

37. Emotional expressions involving a stereotyped sequence of fixed action patterns include

(1) smiling
(2) brow flash response
(3) startle response
(4) apprehension

38. The left hemisphere of the brain is generally associated with

(1) language acquisition
(2) music appreciation
(3) mathematical reasoning
(4) spatioperceptual abilities

39. Which of the following chemicals may act as a neurotransmitter in the nervous system?

(1) Epinephrine
(2) Dopamine
(3) Norepinephrine
(4) Acetylcholine

40. Which of the following neurotransmitters can be directly influenced by diet and eating behaviors?

(1) Acetylcholine
(2) Norepinephrine
(3) Serotonin
(4) Gamma-aminobutyric acid

7 60 yo old - 5.5 hrs/day sleep

41. Dynorphin, a natural brain endorphin, is

   (1) 50 times more potent than any other known endorphin
   (2) able to bind to pain receptors with great specificity
   (3) 200 times more potent than morphine
   (4) clinically useful in more severe pain problems

42. Food intake is controlled by which of the following biochemical indexes?

   (1) Arteriovenous differences in blood glucose levels
   (2) Volume of lipid deposits in the body
   (3) Amino acid content of the blood
   (4) Absolute levels of blood glucose

43. Substances responsive to stress include

   (1) catecholamines
   (2) growth hormone
   (3) endorphins
   (4) adrenocorticotropic hormone (ACTH)

44. Common organic explanations for a sleep disturbance in the healthy individual include

   (1) disruptions of normal circadian rhythms
   (2) accumulation of hepatic enzymes
   (3) the inevitable consequences of aging
   (4) suppressed REM sleep

45. A lesion of the axons of motor neurons that innervate skeletal muscle (lower motor neurons) will result in which of the following behavioral consequences?

   (1) Paralysis of individual muscles on the side of the lesion
   (2) A paradoxical increase in reflex activity
   (3) Reduction in muscle mass (atrophy)
   (4) Increase in muscle tone

46. Perinatal gonadal hormones have a developmental impact on which of the following?

   (1) Sex-linked neural differentiation
   (2) Sexuality in adulthood
   (3) Neural morphology
   (4) The permanent organization of parts of the nervous system

47. The gate control theory of pain is useful because it has

(1) allowed for clinical predictions that have proved empirically useful
(2) encouraged the testing of pharmacological and surgical blocks
(3) reversed emphasis on pain as solely an afferent sensory experience
(4) confirmed a higher central decoding mechanism for control of pain

behaviour affected by environment

48. Ethology is characterized by which of the following concepts?

(1) Sign stimulus or releaser
(2) Study of behavior under natural conditions
(3) Fixed action patterns
(4) Behavior unaffected by environment

49. Human behavioral patterns that have the potential of containing major innate (i.e., genetic, or not learned) components include

(1) intelligence
(2) brow flash response
(3) facial expressions of anger, fear, disgust, and joy
(4) smiling

50. With appropriate reinforcers, operant conditioning can modify which of the following autonomically mediated responses?

(1) Blood pressure
(2) Glomerular filtration rate
(3) Heart rate
(4) Migraine headaches

51. A by-product of the research on the gate control theory of pain was the determination that the pain experience consists of which of the following components?

(1) Sensory-discriminative
(2) Motivational-affective
(3) Cognitive-evaluative
(4) Reflex-reactive

52. True statements about sleeping pills include which of the following?

(1) They lose their effectiveness in about 2 weeks
(2) Barbiturates gradually lead to an increase in hepatic enzymes
(3) Patients develop tolerance for benzodiazepines much less rapidly than for pentobarbital
(4) Barbiturates enhance REM sleep

53. The stimulation of various behavior patterns by amphetamines can be blocked by 6-hydroxydopamine only if there have been prior massive depletions of

(1) gamma-aminobutyric acid
(2) norepinephrine
(3) glutamate
(4) dopamine

54. The seemingly contradictory ability of barbiturates to stimulate behavior at one dosage level and depress it at another can be explained by the

(1) inverted-U relationship between arousal and behavioral efficiency
(2) reduced input of irrelevant stimuli at low doses
(3) attenuation of arousal at high doses
(4) general tranquilizing processes

55. Which of the following can be considered ontogenetic stages of synaptic modification?

(1) Synapse formation under genetic and developmental control
(2) Maintenance of newly developed synapses occurring during critical periods
(3) Regulation of transient and long-term effectiveness of synapses
(4) Establishment of cellular neuropsychology of human mentation

56. Which of the following physiological response patterns will usually accompany dreaming?

(1) Electroencephalographic desynchrony
(2) Rapid eye movements
(3) Loss of sternocleidomastoid tonus
(4) Tachycardia

57. The relationship between social and biological processes in the generation of behavior has historically been classified by which of the following terms?

(1) Conditioned
(2) Organic
(3) Genetic
(4) Functional

58. True statements about the behavioral assessment of alcohol abuse include which of the following?

(1) Individuals with a high degree of acquired tolerance tend to exhibit less evidence of behavioral impairment than those with less tolerance
(2) Trained clinical observers are prone to frequent errors when estimating the actual levels of intoxication of alcohol abusers
(3) Women attain higher blood levels, absorb alcohol faster, and reach peak blood alcohol levels sooner than men
(4) Police officers are more accurate in estimating blood alcohol levels than is a group of social drinkers

59. In the precipitation of coronary disease, the pathophysiological concomitants of stress accompanied by lack of control result in the activation of the

(1) gastrointestinal system
(2) sympathetic adrenal medullary system
(3) immune system
(4) pituitary adrenal cortical axis

60. The use of relaxation techniques for stress reduction affects diabetic patients in which of the following ways?

(1) Significant improvement in glucose tolerance
(2) Increased insulin sensitivity
(3) Unchanged glucose-stimulated insulin secretory activity
(4) Increased plasma cortisol levels

61. Dream deprivation is apt to produce which of the following?

(1) A rebound phenomenon of increased dreaming
(2) An increase in anxiety and irritability
(3) Retardation of memory formation of emotionally toned words
(4) A major decrement in psychological functions

62. There is now increasing evidence that natural killer-cell activity

(1) decreases with the secretion of corticosteroids through the hypothalamic-pituitary-adrenal axis
(2) plays a role in inhibition of tumor growth
(3) deters the spread of both distant and local cancer
(4) increases under conditions of psychosocial stress

63. Metabolic changes occurring during exercise include which of the following

(1) The rate of glucose removal from the blood and plasma increases
(2) The amount of insulin required for glucose uptake decreases
(3) The sensitivity of insulin receptors in skeletal muscle increases
(4) The sensitivity of insulin receptors in adipose tissue decreases

64. Duodenal ulcer activity is exacerbated by

(1) occupational choice
(2) chronic anxiety
(3) socioeconomic status
(4) psychological stress

DIRECTIONS: Each group of questions below consists of lettered headings followed by a set of numbered items. For each numbered item select the **one** lettered heading with which it is **most** closely associated. Each lettered heading may be used **once, more than once, or not at all.**

Questions 65-69

For each description that follows, select the substance with which it is most closely associated.

(A) Dopamine
(B) Dopamine-β-hydroxylase
(C) 6-Hydroxydopamine
(D) Norepinephrine
(E) Acetylcholine

65. Transmitter that ultimately mediates all overt behavior

66. Substance found to be deficient in the brains of schizophrenic persons

67. Substance that poisons neurons by forming peroxides and has been implicated in the cause of schizophrenia

68. Agent that mediates behavioral reward

69. Agent that is a putative transmitter and also a precursor of another transmitter in the brain reward system

Questions 70-74

Select the tissue with which each hormone, pair of hormones, or hormonal activity is most closely associated.

(A) Hypothalamus
(B) Anterior pituitary
(C) Posterior pituitary
(D) Adrenal cortex
(E) Thyroid

70. Oxytocin and vasopressin storage and release

71. Follicle-stimulating hormone (FSH) and luteinizing hormone (LH)

72. Adrenocorticotropic hormone (ACTH)

73. Corticotropin-releasing hormone (CRH)

74. Cortisol

Questions 75-79

For each description, select the drug or drug classification with which it is most closely associated.

(A) Barbiturates
(B) Pentylenetetrazol (Metrazol)
(C) Amphetamine
(D) Cocaine
(E) Meprobamate

75. Addictive sedative that depresses a wide variety of biologic processes

76. Convulsive stimulant that acts primarily on the central nervous system

77. Local anesthetic that produces euphoric activity by its action on the central nervous system

78. Monoamine oxidase inhibitor that has variable appetite-depressing activity

79. Mild tranquilizing agent

Questions 80-85

Match the following descriptions with the appropriate stages of sleep.

(A) Stage 1 REM sleep
(B) Stage 1 NREM sleep
(C) Stages 1 through 4 slow wave sleep (NREM)
(D) Stage 4 delta wave sleep (NREM)
(E) Stage 2 NREM sleep

80. Heart rate, blood pressure, and respiration decline and gastrointestinal movements increase

81. Suppression by alcohol and barbiturates

82. Sleeper more likely to awaken spontaneously

83. Higher frequency of dream recall

84. Of longer duration during the first half of night

85. Continuous decline in the elderly

Questions 86-91

Match the results or situations below with the substances produced by smoking behavior.

(A) Nicotine
(B) Carbon monoxide
(C) Hydrogen cyanide
(D) Both hydrogen cyanide and carbon monoxide
(E) Both nicotine and carbon monoxide

86. Contributes to increased prevalence of fatal and nonfatal cardiovascular disease

87. Promotes chronic obstructive pulmonary disease, emphysema, and chronic bronchitis

88. Valuable in the discrimination of smokers from nonsmokers

89. Individuals obtain pharmacologically satisfying doses and titrate intake by adjusting their smoking behavior

90. Results in decreased oxygen content in fetal blood and subsequent complications in pregnancy

91. Exposure to smoke from other people's cigarettes can lead to elevated blood levels

Questions 92-97

For each condition select the biological system or substance with which it is most closely associated.

(A) Endocrine and autonomic nervous systems
(B) Hypothalamic-limbic-midbrain circuits
(C) Adrenal cortex and thyroid
(D) Neuropeptides
(E) Dopaminergic circuit or system

92. Highly relevant for Parkinson's disease and schizophrenia

93. Active in mediating integrative processes relevant to survival

94. Substantially involved in mediating adaptive functions of memory appraisal and motivational-emotional responses

95. Active in "fine tuning" one's mood

96. Especially active when one becomes very upset, angry, or depressed for an extended period of time

97. Coordinated by the hypothalamus

Questions 98-102

For each combination of rearing and sibling relatedness, select the IQ correlation coefficient with which it is most closely associated.

(A) 0.92
(B) 0.86
(C) 0.53
(D) 0.50
(E) 0.42

C 98. Fraternal twins reared together

A 99. Identical twins reared together

B 100. Identical twins reared apart

D 101. Siblings reared together

E 102. Siblings reared apart

Questions 103-110

For each psychological response, select the biological system or anatomical region with which it is most closely associated.

(A) Sympatho-adrenomedullary system
(B) Hypothalamic-pituitary-adrenocortical (HPAC) system
(C) Immune system
(D) Endorphin-enkephalin system
(E) Anterior hypothalamus

C 103. Suppressed by stress

A 104. Increased metabolic activity in response to stress

B 105. A "conservation-withdrawal" pattern

D 106. Reduction of fear and pain in aversive situations

B 107. Peptic ulceration and clinical depression

A 108. Implicated in hypertension, angina pectoris, and cardiac arrhythmia

C 109. Suppressed by increased lympholytic steroid hormones

E 110. The relaxation response

Biological Correlates and Behavioral Medicine Answers

1. The answer is C. *(Carlson, ed 3. pp 119-121.)* Most glands receive either direct neural control from the brain or indirect control from hormones secreted by the hypothalamus. Thus, thyroid secretion is subject to hypothalamic control, whereas insulin secretion depends in part on adrenergic influence from the autonomic nervous system. The parathyroids are notably free of brain control; in regulating calcium metabolism, they in turn are regulated by blood levels of calcium.

2. The answer is B. *(Carlson, ed 3. pp 378-386.)* Oxytocin is one of the peptide hormones that apparently is behaviorally inactive. It has an important function in parturition by facilitating contractions of the uterus; the hormone also facilitates ejection of milk during lactation. The gonadal steroids, in contrast, exert profound effects on behavior. They are necessary for appropriate reproductive and parental behavior patterns in any species of mammals. In addition, gonadal hormones mediate many forms of agonistic behavior.

3. The answer is D. *(Plomin, pp 284-285.)* The risk of schizophrenia in the general population is about 1 percent. Studies of the risks for relatives of schizophrenics reveal that schizophrenia runs in families. Siblings of schizophrenics are approximately eight times more likely to become schizophrenic than are persons chosen randomly from the population; this rate almost doubles when those siblings have an affected parent as well as an affected sibling. The risk is no greater when the mother is schizophrenic than when the father is schizophrenic. If both parents are schizophrenic, the risk becomes four times as great as when only one parent is schizophrenic. Grandchildren of schizophrenics have about twice the risk as the general population since grandchildren share about one-fourth of the grandparent's segregating genes; great-grandchildren (sharing about one-eighth of the genes) have a slightly more than average chance of becoming schizophrenic.

4. The answer is C. *(Plomin, pp 154-174.)* Almost all chromosomal abnormalities influence general cognitive ability and growth. Down's syndrome is the most frequent genetic cause of mental retardation. It often bears a strong relationship to maternal age. Persons with Down's syndrome have 47 chromosomes instead of the normal 46. The syndrome was originally named trisomy 21 because, at the time, the trisomy was thought to involve the next to the smallest autosome (number 21 by the Denver system of enumeration). It is now known that the smallest autosome is the one in triplicate. Even though Down's syndrome should really be called trisomy 22, the error is so firmly entrenched in the literature that it is still referred to as involving chromosome 21. Turner's syndrome (XO) occurs in females with the absence of one of the two X chromosomes. Although most sufferers have a normal IQ, Turner's syndrome nearly always involves sterility, with some limited secondary sexual development. Individuals with Klinefelter's syndrome (XXY) are phenotypic males with an extra X chromosome. About 1 percent of males institutionalized for retardation have Klinefelter's syndrome. Bartholin-Patau syndrome (trisomy 13) and Edwards' syndrome (trisomy 18) are caused by trisomy of chromosomes 13 and 18, respectively. Sufferers are characterized as severely retarded, and most die in the first few months of life.

5.   The answer is B. *(Kandel, ed 2. pp 188-189.)* When the axon is cut, the axon and synaptic terminals are deprived of essential metabolic connections with the cell body. Since axonal transport occurs in both directions, the result is a rapid local degeneration of the axon and myelin sheath, with the cell body also being affected. Synapses mediate both electrical signals and nutritive interactions between neurons. Thus, changes occur in the cell body (retrograde changes) and also in subsequent neurons that receive synapses from the damaged neurons. Macrophages from the general circulation enter the trauma area and phagocytose axonal debris, and glial cells (astrocytes and microglia) proliferate to assist in the process. This proliferation of fibrous astrocytes forms a glial scar around the trauma area, which can then block the course of regenerating axons and the reformation of central connections. The behavioral effects of nerve lesions are peculiar to the location of the lesion in the brain and the nerve cell connections, so that the same type of injury will have different behavioral effects depending on its location.

6.   The answer is E. *(Kandel, ed 2. pp 811-814.)* Memory can be divided into short-term and long-term stages. Recently acquired memories are more easily disrupted by such factors as trauma, whereas long-term memories, or older memories, are fairly resistant to disturbance. Short-term memory is transformed into a more permanent long-term store. Thus, the memory process is always undergoing continual change with time. Both short-term and long-term memories are encoded in neural activity that involves a physical change in the brain with apparent alterations of the connections between neurons. It is also clear that the memory traces are not localized to any one brain structure, and that all parts of the nervous system have the plastic properties needed for memory storage. The recall involves an active reconstruction rather than a faithful reproduction of the internal store, and the complex nature of learning itself ensures that the involved neurons are widely distributed in the nervous system. Fortunately, the brain has the capacity to take limited remaining information (memory) and reconstruct a relatively good reproduction of the original memory.

The temporal lobes and associated areas and the hippocampus are not registers or banks for memory storage but are actively involved in the storage and retrieval process. Since memory traces are not localized in any one brain structure, trauma to one part of the nervous system can create initial memory loss, but some memory gradually returns even though the lesion or trauma seemed to have caused complete amnesia.

7. The answer is D. *(Kandel, ed 2. pp 718-725.)* Clinical studies of patients with major depressive disorders indicate that an intrinsic regulatory defect involving the hypothalamus underlies the disorder. It also involves the monoamine pathways. The hypothalamic modulation of neuroendocrine activity has been implicated, as have been the neurotransmitter systems of serotonin and norepinephrine. Recent evidence suggests a major role for the heritability of such neurochemical disorders. The role of behavior in stimulating or triggering such mechanisms is also being explored. While the frontal lobes, the pituitary, the hippocampus, and the corpus callosum are related to the emotions, memory, and neural communications, they do not play as major a role in the depressive disorders as does the hypothalamus.

8. The answer is C. *(Kandel, ed 2. pp 757-766.)* All functions of the brain represent an interaction between genetic and environmental factors (e.g., learning). It is also known that the structure of the brain is greatly influenced by genetic and developmental processes. It is not always appreciated that the structure of the brain, specifically the pattern of interconnections between the neurons, also depends on experience with behavior. This influence is established early, in that there are certain critical stages in the development of the brain when the integrative action of the brain and its cellular structure are dependent upon its interaction with its environment. Further, the work of Harry Harlow with isolated young monkeys, the work of Rene Spitz and others with early human sensory and social deprivation, and the early sensory deprivation perception studies of von Senden, Riesen, Hubel, and Wiesel have soundly established the importance of the critical period concept upon the development of normal social behavior, physical growth, and normal visual perception. The influence and the action of the environment on the brain do vary with age—both normal and abnormal patterns of stimulation having a more profound effect at early stages of development. Environmental stimuli, social experience, and learning and memory also continue to have an influence on adults.

9. The answer is D. *(Winefield, pp 28-36.)* Ethology in psychology and biology has made a number of conceptual contributions to understanding human behavior through the comparative study of animal behavior in relation to natural habitat. Ethologists have found evidence to suggest that some aspects of human behavior may be a function of species-membership in the form of predispositions to learn and respond in certain ways rather than the fixed sequences of motor activity found in lower animals. The fixed action pattern is a genetically established sequence of motor activity that is triggered by a sign-stimulus that is sufficient to release the fixed action pattern of behavior. These links between sign-stimulus and fixed action pattern are weaker and more variable in humans because of the overriding effects of experience and learning. However, certain predispositions to respond to certain stimuli in certain ways are presently being explored. Imprinting is the tendency of very young animals to become fixed-on and follow a member of their own species (usually their mother, but another animal or even an object can be substituted). The period of development when there is maximum receptivity to these crucial cues is known as the critical period. Bond formation between infants and adults does occur in both humans and lower animals, but ethnic bonds appear to be almost totally learned rather than biologically established.

10. The answer is B. *(Kandel, ed 2. pp 679-680.)* In the 1940s, prefrontal lobotomy appeared to be effective in reducing patient anxiety, but subsequent controlled studies did not confirm this effect. In fact, prefrontal lobotomy was increasingly associated with a high incidence of complications such as epilepsy, abnormal personality changes, lack of inhibition, and lack of initiative and drive. On the other hand, there was no apparent reduction in intellectual capability as measured by intelligence tests.

11. The answer is C. *(Plomin, pp 167-169.)* Persons with Klinefelter's syndrome, a genetic disorder of men, exhibit a variety of male morphologic and behavioral characteristics. This phenomenon is attributed to the extra X (male) chromosomes in such a person's genotype (XXY). These persons represent nearly 1 percent of males institutionalized for retardation, epilepsy, or mental illness. The incidence in the general population is 2 per 1,000 newborn males. They generally have abnormally small testes, low levels of male hormone (testosterone), and sterility. In spite of a high incidence of mental retardation, about 75 percent have IQs within the normal range.

12. The answer is C. *(Plomin, pp 355-357.)* Earlier studies of several decades ago calculated that heritability accounted for about 70 to 75 percent of the total variation in IQ scores within a family. More recent studies involving much larger samples show that the individual differences in general cognitive ability within families is actually closer to 50 percent. Inheritance is still a major factor in the development of individual differences in IQ, since no specific environmental influence has been found to account for even as much as 10 percent of the variance in IQ scores within families.

13. The answer is B. *(Thompson, pp 49-50.)* Complex behavioral traits such as schizophrenia, which may vary widely in nature from person to person, are considered to involve anomalies at more than one gene locus. The science of behavior genetics deals with the quantitative analysis of these polygenic traits. The results of a great variety of investigations now favor the view that schizophrenia is a genetically determined disorder.

14. The answer is C. *(Plomin, pp 8, 110-114.)* Phenylketonuria (PKU) results from the inheritance of a double recessive gene. Affected persons suffer an inability to metabolize phenylalanine, a common amino acid in food. If the condition is undetected in time for treatment with special diets, serious mental deficiency results, presumably as a consequence of the toxic effect of abnormal blood levels of phenylpyruvic acid on the developing brain. About 1 percent of institutionalized retarded persons are retarded because of PKU. Most PKU individuals do not become mentally retarded if they are given a diet low in phenylalanine during the developing years. Early identification of affected infants combined with replacement of milk with galactose-free substances has been quite successful in reducing the subsequent mental retardation. PKU is a good example of genes affecting behavior in the same way genes affect phenotypes. It also provides an example of an environmental intervention successfully bypassing a genetic problem.

15. The answer is D. *(Weiss, 1984. pp 44-54.)* Behavioral factors influence the development of coronary heart disease through the cardiovascular or endocrine correlates of sympathetic-adrenal-medullary and pituitary-adrenal-cortical activity. The following mechanisms are currently considered to be most involved: (1) behavioral stressors can promote arterial injury through hemodynamic forces, such as turbulence and sheer stress caused by repeated physiological reactions of excessive heart rate and pressor response; (2) biochemical sources of injury may exert toxic influences on coronary arteries through behaviorally caused increases in endocrines such as catecholamines and corticosteroids; (3) increased circulating catecholamines may affect atherogenesis through influences on platelet aggregation and on the mobilization of serum lipids; (4) acute behavioral stressors can lower the thresholds for ventricular fibrillation; and (5) central nervous system control of the heart can initiate arrhythmic activity, potentially precipitating sudden cardiac death.

16. The answer is D. *(Schneiderman, pp 243-249.)* Behavioral methods have been developed to treat both the psychological and physiological aspects of many diseases that have been formerly regarded as exclusively organic. Of the treatments for cardiovascular diseases, those for hypertension and arrhythmias have successfully benefited from behavioral interventions. In hypertension, relaxation procedures have been effective in controlling pressure, particularly mild hypertension, producing a decrease of 5 to 12 mm Hg. Arrhythmias can be regulated by biofeedback and relaxation in some patients, and heart rate can be controlled in most patients. Heart block cannot be controlled, particularly third-degree heart block, in which neural control of heart rate is not possible. However, behavioral intervention can be a judicious adjunct to drugs and other treatments. Raynaud's disease (and migraine headache) can be effectively treated with temperature biofeedback and relaxation procedures. Asthma has been treated in some patients by relaxation, self-control, and stress control. Placebo effects are also helpful. Asthma and hypertension, as well as many other diseases, can be treated effectively with behavioral intervention and conjoint use of drugs and other treatments.

17. The answer is C. *(Williams, vol 2. pp 6-7.)* Under stressful conditions, the organism secretes endorphins and ACTH together. Pro-opiocortin is a common precursor. The close link between endorphins and ACTH suggests that they serve a mediation function for a closely related set of adaptation responses. Thus, they can facilitate one's response to stress and at the same time help one to withstand pain and mobilize for coping activity to deal with the stressful challenge or threat.

18. The answer is A. *(Lindzey, ed 3. pp 855-859.)* Epinephrine and norepinephrine (catecholamines) secretion, which is accelerated under conditions of psychosocial stress, induces pathogenic states leading to cardiovascular disease, for example, increased blood pressure and heart rate, elevated blood lipids, acceleration of the rate of damage to the inner areas of the coronary arteries, and also the induction or provocation of ventricular arrhythmias. First degree AV block is a conduction disorder unrelated to stress. The provocation of ventricular arrhythmias is especially important as a potential cause of sudden death.

19. The answer is E. *(Iversen, ed 2. p 231.)* Although neuroses are highly variable in nature, most involve anxiety and tension. In the treatment of persons suffering from neurotic anxiety, except for meprobamate the minor tranquilizers—benzodiazepines in particular—are to be preferred to barbiturates because of the tolerance and dependence associated with the latter. Although dependence is frequently established in the use of minor tranquilizers, it is more quickly and severely established with barbiturates. Barbiturates also present an increased hazard from accidental overdose or suicide. The minor tranquilizers have been demonstrated to be more effective in the treatment of anxiety. Barbiturates are CNS depressants, thus increasing depressive aspects of a neurosis.

20. The answer is E. *(Lindzey, ed 3. pp 859-860.)* If a person is agitated, anxious, in a state of panic or near panic, or in a state of hypervigilance to minor or major threat cues, increased breathing (hyperventilation) is a frequent response. Typically, a series of major physiological, behavioral, and psychological changes are evoked. The reduced CO_2 in the blood lowers the blood acid level, sympathetic activity increases, cardiac arrhythmias increase, heart rate increases, decreased oxygen is supplied to brain tissue, and there is heightened cerebral vasoconstriction. Acute anxiety ensues, generally focused on the threatening situation or somatic complaints, and there is a heightened sense of fear. The altered patterns of vascular, neurological, and cerebral activity are mainly responsible for the psychomotor and cognitive impairments. Such psychological, social, physical, or environmental hypervigilance frequently results in temporary impairment and defective decision-making characterized by excessive vacillation and an impulsive choice of options.

21. The answer is D. *(Carlson, ed 3. pp 328-335.)* More is known about the effects of depriving an individual of various kinds of sleep, such as dream sleep, than about the effects of total sleep deprivation. There appears to be a need for a certain amount of dream sleep. A deficiency produces a "rebound" phenomenon of increased dreaming when uninterrupted sleep is permitted. Contrary to earlier speculations, dream deprivation does not produce any major impairment in psychological functions, nor does it produce any impairment of performance on simple verbal tasks with no emotional content. Dream sleep deprivation, however, does impair the recall of emotionally toned words. It somehow assists the integration of emotional material with memories of other experiences. A major effect of dream deprivation is that it retards memory formation. An interesting variation is that new learning experiences result in an increase in subsequent dream sleep.

22. The answer is D. *(Thompson, p 330.)* Stanley Schachter (1974) observed that food intake regulation in obese persons is rather similar to that in rats that have hypothalamic hyperphagia. Such persons and rats both are strongly influenced by the taste (and, in humans, appearance) of food. Consequently, food-ingestive behavior may be quite independent of physiological need in both species.

23. The answer is E. *(Weiss, 1981. pp 311-317.)* Stress studies utilizing such situations as preavoidance conditioning, postsurgical convalescence, exposure to cold conditions, and other stressful conditions have been shown to produce a significant increase in certain physiological measures. The most recent findings involving the stress of preavoidance conditioning have shown significant increases in systolic and diastolic blood pressure, plasma potassium, and plasma sodium, with decreases in heart rate. These behaviorally induced changes in potassium are significant because they are known to increase the secretion of aldosterone, which is the most potent of the salt-retaining hormones. Behavioral conditioning procedures are also known to produce increases in ACTH and renin-angiotensin, which can vary the levels of aldosterone. The interactions between these behaviorally induced physiological measures is significantly related to the development of chronic elevation of blood pressure.

24. The answer is D. *(Weiss, 1981. pp 31-34, 321-328.)* The incidence and prevalence of coronary heart disease caused by atherosclerosis have been linked to the type A coronary-prone behavior pattern. Individuals who are considered to be type A are more prone to respond to environmental challenges (social, psychological, or physical) with increased physiological responses. These behaviorally induced physiological responses over a lifetime appear to be linked to the development of certain cardiovascular pathologies. Laboratory studies of humans have found that type A individuals exhibit an increased level of systolic blood pressure, heart rate, plasma norepinephrine, plasma epinephrine, and cortisol and a decrease in occipital alpha activity. Other increases associated with coronary heart disease include serum cholesterol, serum triglycerides, platelet aggregation, clotting time, and serum corticotropin.

25. The answer is E. *(Rosen, pp 114-116.)* Vigorous exercise over time has been shown to increase the high-density lipoprotein cholesterol in the blood while decreasing the low-density lipoprotein cholesterol, very low-density lipoprotein cholesterol, total cholesterol, and triglycerides. Thus, vigorous exercise acts to reduce several established coronary heart disease risk factors and to promote increased high-density lipoprotein cholesterol, which apparently has an antiatherogenic effect.

26. The answer is C. *(Kaplan, ed 4. pp 45-53.)* In the late 1950s, Harry Harlow discovered that monkeys reared with a terry cloth-covered substitute mother were much more likely to engage in effective heterosexual relationships as juveniles than were monkeys raised with a steel wire substitute mother. He concluded that the comfort provided by the clothed (or natural) mother was a critical precursor of the feeling of love. He also demonstrated its importance for social and emotional development.

27. The answer is B. *(Carlson, ed 3. pp 497-499.)* In most species, the male tends to be more aggressive than the female. Animal handlers long have taken advantage of the fact that castration, by reducing aggression, makes animals more tractable. Testosterone administered postpubertally to castrated rats can restore aggressiveness to almost normal levels. Similarly, neonatal female mice develop masculine aggressive behavior on receiving androgens. Androgens also promote aggression in humans. Boys are more aggressive than girls at ages 3 to 10, as has been demonstrated in studies of male and female children. Criminals with a history of violence have also been found to have differences in testosterone levels, but it is not yet certain whether the higher androgen levels promote violence or the aggression increases the androgen levels. Probably both mechanisms are active.

28. The answer is B. *(Weiss, 1981. pp 371-400.)* Psychosocial stress, whether experimentally or environmentally induced, has been shown to produce increased levels of adrenal corticoids. This is accomplished through neuroendocrine pathways involving the cerebral cortex, the hypothalamus, the pituitary, and the adrenal cortex. The direct effect of such stress-induced plasma cortisone elevation is injury to various components of the immune system, and this injury results in increased vulnerability to the subsequent action of latent oncogenic viruses, newly mutated cancer cells, or other pathological processes that are normally prevented by normally functioning immunological surveillance mechanisms. As an example, increased blood levels of glucocorticoids over an extended period of time have a lytic effect on lymphocytes and on lymphatic tissues such as the thymus, nodes, and spleen. Thus their depletion enhances various pathological processes, including that of cancer.

29. The answer is C. *(Suinn, pp 416-419.)* General paresis, also known as dementia paralytica, is the progressive impairment of cognitive, affective, and motor functioning that is a manifestation of advanced syphilis. The infecting organism, the spirochete *Treponema pallidum,* is detectable by cerebrospinal fluid and blood analysis. If unchecked, the spirochete may cause irreversible neurological damage, resulting in memory deterioration, delusional ideas, and, eventually, terminal paralysis. The disease can be treated effectively if diagnosed before the onset of the advanced phase. While paresis is uncommon today, one must be alert to its possibility.

30. The answer is E. *(Last, ed 12, pp 1319-1320, 1430-1432.)* Down's syndrome (mongolism) is caused by a chromosomal aberration. Most sufferers have 47 chromosomes instead of 46. The risk of Down's syndrome increases dramatically with maternal age, especially after age 35. The general incidence is about 1:700 live births, varying from about 1:2000 live births in early child-bearing age to about 1:400 at age 35 and about 1:100 at age 40. About 80 percent of Down's syndrome infants will have standard trisomy, about 15 percent will have the translocation form, and 5 percent will have the mosaic form. About one-third of the translocation cases are inherited and detectable in one or the other parent. Amniocentesis can detect the presence of Down's syndrome, but the procedure requires surgical skill, is not free from hazard, and, if the test is positive, introduces ethical and religious considerations of potential induced abortion. Down's syndrome accounts for about 30 percent of the retarded children in the United States. Although some sufferers have a relatively normal IQ, most IQs are between 40 and 60. Most used to die early, but with antibiotics and other scientific advances, those who live to the preschool age can now be expected to live to the average age of 40.

31. The answer is C. *(Feuerstein, pp 433-437.)* The gate control theory of pain has demonstrated that pain is more than the single transmission from the pain source to the brain. Actually, pain is the net result of neurophysiological and neurochemical processes that permit psychological factors such as motivation, emotion, and cognition (including memory) to modulate the pain experience. Cognitive factors are known to influence even spinal withdrawal reflexes; for example, a hot object that is valuable will be handled more carefully than another object that can be dropped safely. The spinal gate mechanism is in the substantia gelatinosa in the dorsal horn and is influenced by the relative amount of activity of the large-diameter rapidly conducting fibers (which inhibit transmission and close the gate) in comparison with the small-diameter low fibers (which facilitate and open the gate). The spinal gate mechanism can be influenced (inhibited) by cognitive factors that descend from the brain, and by neuropeptide release. Even though the theory is not completely confirmed, it has resulted in the important clinical application of enabling physicians to diminish pain by stimulating the large-diameter dorsal column fibers to close the gate. The theory has also rejected the notion of pain as solely an afferent sensory experience.

32. The answer is C. *(Doleys, pp 84-90.)* The behavioral medicine technique of measuring blood flow in the finger and raising the temperature through biofeedback has been found to be very effective in the relief of the migraine headache. The rationale is that since the arousal of the sympathetic nervous system produces vasoconstriction in the periphery, then training patients to increase the peripheral blood flow in their fingers teaches them to relax the sympathetic outflow, thereby inducing a general bodily relaxation. Alpha EEG biofeedback produces relaxation and has been used with some success, but less than that with finger temperature biofeedback. Frontalis EMG biofeedback has been more effective in the treatment of anxiety asthma, essential hypertension, and tension headache. Hypnosis and psychotherapy have not proved to be effective in the treatment of migraine headaches.

33. The answer is E. *(Hamburg, pp 124-133.)* Most of the characteristic risk factors of cardiovascular disease are behavioral. The usual factors of hypertension, cholesterolemia, and cigarette smoking have basic behavioral bases, particularly in terms of stress, diet, and behavioral addictions, but others such as obesity, personality type, and physical inactivity are also behaviorally based. Advanced age, maleness, and diabetes are less behaviorally related (but still have behavioral components). A high concentration of glucose without overt diabetes is both behaviorally (via diet) and metabolically related. A small amount of alcohol consumption appears to decrease risk, but excessive amounts increase risk, especially when combined with smoking behavior and type A personality.

34. The answer is A (1, 2, 3). *(Braunwald, ed 11. pp 2108-2109.)* Family, twin, and adoption studies support the importance of genetic factors in alcoholism. Close relatives of alcoholics have a fourfold increased risk, which is still true even if the children of alcoholics are given up for adoption at birth without the alcohol problems of their parents being known. The fourfold increased risk of close relatives for alcoholism does not make them significantly more vulnerable for other psychiatric illnesses. Twin research has shown that the risk for the identical twin of an alcoholic is about 60 percent and the concordance rate for fraternal twins is only about 30 percent.

35. The answer is E (all). *(Schuster, ed 2. p 329.)* Seven significant variables potentially influence one's gender identity. They are (1) chromosomal configuration (XX or XY), (2) gonad endowment (ovaries or testes), (3) internal reproductive structures (uterus or prostate), (4) external genitalia (vagina or penis), (5) hormonal balance (estrogen or androgen), (6) gender assigned at birth, and (7) response of the parents to the child's assigned gender.

36. The answer is E (all). *(Ader, pp 229-257.)* A number of experimental and clinical studies on the effects of psychosocial stress on the human immune system have demonstrated a decrease in natural killer-cell activity in healthy human subjects. Likewise, stress was related to a decrease in lymphocyte cytotoxicity and a decrease in the rate of microbe engulfment by polymorphonuclear granulocytes. There was also a depression in the T-lymphocyte response to mitogens. Another study demonstrated that sleep deprivation decreased the ability of blood neutrophil granulocytes to phagocytize *Staphylococcus aureus* and increased the production of interferon by blood lymphocytes. Also, the phytohemagglutinin-induced DNA synthesis of blood lymphocytes was reduced after a sleep deprivation period of 48 hours.

37. The answer is A (1, 2, 3). *(Kandel, ed 2. pp 801-802.)* Humans have a number of simple behaviors that resemble the fixed action patterns of lower animals. Such emotional expressions as the startle response and smiling are stereotyped sequences of movements. In human infants, smiling appears to be under the control of a specific sign stimulus. Studies show that the smiling response is not triggered by the face as a whole, but rather by certain specific features. For example, the eyes are of particular importance as a sign stimulus, and as the child matures, the brow flash response (rapid raising and dropping of eyebrows) is a stereotyped response present in widely different cultures. A complex set of human behaviors that is universal in emotional expression across cultures includes the facial expressions of anger, fear, disgust, and joy.

38. The answer is B (1, 3). *(Ornstein, pp 36-40.)* While the control of certain intellectual functions by the right hemisphere or left hemisphere is not as clear-cut and clearly divided as was once thought, there are still general functions related to the right or left hemisphere. The left hemisphere is much more involved in language and logic and the right is much more involved in spatial abilities and "gestalt" thinking, even though both hemispheres do interact with each other. If one hemisphere (e.g., the left) is damaged at birth, the other hemisphere can take over some of the language function. This becomes less easy with age.

39. The answer is E (all). *(Brown, pp 38-39.)* Neuroscientists now generally agree that there are over a dozen chemicals that act as neurotransmitters in the nervous system. It is hypothesized that even more will eventually be found. At present the chemicals most involved as neurotransmitters are acetylcholine, norepinephrine, dopamine, serotonin, epinephrine, and gamma-aminobutyric acid.

40. The answer is A (1, 2, 3). *(Miller, pp 60-65.)* Not all neurotransmitters are influenced by diet, but acetylcholine, serotonin, and norepinephrine have been demonstrated to be subject to dietary control. Since the enzyme catalyzing the rate-limiting step in the formation of each neurotransmitter is relatively unsaturated with substrate, the diet (eating behavior) influences an actual increase or decrease by providing more or less respective precursors available to the brain neurons. Thus, an increase or decrease in the amount of choline rapidly stimulates or decreases the rate of acetylcholine formation. Likewise, serotonin and norepinephrine will be increased or decreased by raising or lowering the precursor levels of brain tryptophan or brain tyrosine (or phenylalanine), respectively.

41. The answer is A (1, 2, 3). *(Williams, RB, pp 3-9.)* Research on hypothalamic hormones has led to the discovery of many neuropeptides. The study of endorphins that bind to various opiate receptors in the brain has led to some amazing discoveries. Dynorphin, a natural brain endorphin, is reported to be 200 times more potent than morphine and 50 times more potent than other known endorphins. The high degree of potency indicates that it is able to bind with great specificity to pain receptors. While it is highly potent, it is still experimental and not in clinical use.

42. The answer is A (1, 2, 3). *(Carlson, ed 3. pp 449-456.)* Arteriovenous differences in blood glucose levels reflect central utilization of glucose and are related to feeding behavior. The *absolute* level of blood glucose, however, is not a major factor. For example, untreated diabetic persons have extremely high blood glucose levels and yet are usually very hungry. These high levels result from a lack of insulin and the body's consequent inability to utilize blood glucose. Therefore, the body is in a fasting state that an affected person perceives as hunger. Amounts of fat deposited in the body and amino acid content of the blood also are factors that control eating.

43. The answer is E (all). *(Hamburg, pp 64-71.)* The catecholamines (e.g., epinephrine, norepinephrine), which are found in the adrenal medulla and in the brain, as well as corticosteroids of the adrenal cortex, have been linked to stress for many years. The endorphins, which are morphine-like peptides found in the brain, pituitary gland, and adrenals, are also linked to stress and are involved in perception of and response to pain. Adrenocorticotropic hormone (ACTH) has been related to stress through control of the adrenal cortex and is present in many neurons in various regions of the brain. A recently identified peptide that stimulates the secretion of ACTH is thought to be the key signal that mediates and integrates an individual's endocrine, visceral, and behavioral responses to stress. ACTH is also linked to beta-endorphin. ACTH and endorphins appear to be secreted together under stress conditions that are perceived by an individual as being dangerous or threatening. Many other hormones are responsive to stress, e.g., prolactin, growth hormone, insulin, testosterone, and luteinizing hormone.

44. The answer is B (1, 3). *(Kandel, ed 2. pp 659-662.)* About 30 to 35 percent of the people who cannot sleep have a relatively simple organic cause for the problem. The two most frequent organic causes are disruptions of normal circadian rhythms and the inevitable consequences of aging. The most common disruptions of normal circadian rhythms are related to travel, "jet lag," and behavioral changes in one's normal daily routine, such as napping, irregular sleep hours and conditions, alteration in meal times, and unusual work schedules. Normal aging is also a major factor as it is more difficult to reset one's biological clock the older one gets. It has been estimated that most people over age 60 sleep only about 5.5 hours per day, and since stage 4 NREM sleep also declines with age, the lighter stages of NREM sleep allow the person to awaken more often, sometimes generating the worry that one cannot sleep or that one is not getting enough sleep. Accumulation of hepatic enzymes is most often the result of prolonged use of sleeping pills.

45. The answer is B (1, 3). *(Kandel, ed 2. pp 188-189.)* The cutting of a nerve tract within the brain or a peripheral nerve results in the following sequence: Both ends of the cut axon immediately seal off the axoplasm, retract, and begin to swell; there is rapid degeneration of the axon and the myelin sheath; the macrophages from the general circulation enter the area and phagocytose axonal debris; there is also a proliferation of glial cells, which act as phagocytes; and fibrous astrocytes proliferate in the central nervous system, which leads to glial scar formation around the zone of trauma, often blocking the course taken by regenerating axons and causing a barrier against the reformation of central connections. Degeneration spreads along the axon in both directions from the zone of trauma. The retrograde reaction in the proximal segment usually progresses a short distance and appears in the cell body after 2 to 3 days. In the distal segment, degeneration appears in the axon terminal in about 1 day, and within 2 weeks the distal synapses degenerate completely.

46. The answer is E (all). *(Kandel, ed 2. pp 772-782.)* Recent evidence has shown that there are morphological and functional differences in the nervous system of males and females. It is known that hormonal deficiencies during early development may result in two syndromes: Turner's syndrome, an anhormonal state in which gonadal tissue does not form (resulting in a phenotypic female, but one who fails to show pubertal changes), and androgen insensitivity syndrome, which is primarily associated with genetic males. (This latter syndrome was formerly called testicular feminization, but persons afflicted with it do not have feminizing testes and do not secrete estrogen-type hormones; they possess abnormal genes and are indistinguishable from phenotypic females in external appearance and psychosexual orientation and libidinal interests.) It is thought that this genetic disorder prevents or blocks responsiveness to androgens throughout development. It is also known that fetal exposure to heterotypical steroid hormones (hormones of one sex given to or influenced by the hormones of another sex) can cause hermaphroditism in genetic females. If, during the fetal period, the female fetus is exposed to an unusual amount of male hormone, the female organ development is distorted, partially reversing the differentiation of the peripheral sex apparatus. The adult sexual behavior of hermaphroditic females is also altered. Thus, the effect is not only on the differentiation of external genitalia, but also on the differentiation of neural tissues that mediate later patterns of sexual behavior. The developing nervous system of both genders is considered to be bipotential. While the female anatomical and behavioral patterns can develop in either an anhormonal or maternal-dominated prenatal environment, the active influence of androgens is required for the development of a male pattern. Furthermore, there is a critical time period during which specific interactions between the developing brain and its environment (internal and external) will mold neuronal and behavioral capabilities. There is increasing evidence that the effects of the perinatal male hormones upon subsequent sexual behavior are more upon the developing central nervous system than upon the peripheral sexual apparatus.

47. The answer is B (1, 3). *(Kandel, ed 2. pp 335-336.)* The gate control theory of pain was developing in the 1960s because of an interest in discovering mechanisms whereby other cutaneous stimuli and emotional states could alter the level of pain felt. It was postulated that the collateral input from large-fiber (Aβ touch fibers) and small-fiber (Aδ and C fibers) interactions in the dorsal horn have an antagonistic effect on cells in the substantia gelatinosa. These were designated as gate cells that regulated the firing of cells deeper in the dorsal horn (probably lamina V) that give rise to the paleospinothalamic tract. Thus, a higher central decoding mechanism was hypothesized—one that monitored spinothalamic activity during which pain is felt. It was also postulated that the brain exerted descending control because cognitive factors could even influence spinal withdrawal reflexes. Subsequent experiments have found very little physiological evidence for the gate control theory, although the negative results are probably not definitive. The gate control theory has persisted because some of its clinical predictions have proven empirically useful (e.g., stimulation of large-diameter dorsal column fibers can provide clinical pain relief for long periods). Furthermore, the emphasis of past research upon pain as solely an afferent sensory experience has been reversed so that the unique and motivational properties of pain (disruption of behavior, a primary negative reinforcer) are now recognized. Attempts to use pharmacological and surgical blocks exclusively prevent several modalities of treatment and can delay attempts to understand how the brain inhibits the perception of pain.

48. The answer is A (1, 2, 3). *(Kandel, ed 2. pp 795-801.)* Ethology was developed by Konrad Lorenz and Nicholaas Tinbergen during the period from 1920 to 1950 by conducting comparative studies of behavior with special emphasis on its mechanisms, ontogeny, and evolution. They emphasized the study of behavior under natural conditions and recognized that all behavior is the result of the interaction between the animal's genetic endowment and the animal's internal and external environment. Innate behavior is a relatively complex sequence of responses, called a fixed action pattern, which is triggered by a sign stimulus or releaser. Thus, behavior patterns (e.g., mating) in lower animals can be activated by a specific stimulus (e.g., the male stickleback fish develops a bright red abdomen [the sign stimulus] that triggers mating behavior [fixed action patterns] of the female). A fixed action pattern, somewhat like a reflex, does not require previous learning for its expression.

49. The answer is E (all). *(Kandel, ed 2. pp 795-803.)* Even though most research on innate behavior has been done on nonmammalian species, nonhuman primates also exhibit innate behavior with innate releasing mechanisms. Some studies with humans demonstrated innate (i.e., genetic, or not learned) determinants of human behavior (e.g., hormonal determinants of gender identity). Since genes control so much of the formation and organization of the basic components of all behavior, including human behavior, behavior must to some extent be under genetic control. Inherited factors nearly always depend on the interaction of genetic and environmental factors in order to be expressed. Some severe mental illnesses, such as schizophrenia, Down's syndrome, and bipolar depression, have known hereditary human behavior factors. Intelligence also has a strong genetic component. Certain human behaviors are universal across cultures—for example, deep tendon reflexes, the eyeblink, and startle reflexes. There are also common drives and needs—for example, hunger, thirst, and sex, and probably the need for social contact and a number of sensory experiences. Certain emotional expressions and facial motor patterns are also universal—for example, facial expressions of anger, fear, disgust, and joy. Infant smiling is a stereotyped behavior that appears to be controlled by a specific sign stimulus, not always in response to another smiling human face. The brow flash response is also stereotyped and consists of a rapid raising and dropping of the eyebrows as a part of the greeting response between persons who know each other.

50. The answer is E (all). *(Leigh, ed 2. pp 394-395.)* The autonomic nervous system was once thought to be completely self-regulating and completely independent of learning or conditioning. The pioneering work of Neil Miller and others, however, has demonstrated that its responses can be modified by appropriate reinforcement. Autonomically mediated responses such as blood pressure, glomerular filtration rate, heart rate, migraine headaches, cardiac arrhythmias, and visceral responses can be modified through operant conditioning. Using learning mechanisms it is now possible to modify or correct such pathological conditions. It must also be emphasized that autonomic responses can be modified so as to produce pathological conditions.

51. The answer is A (1, 2, 3). *(Feuerstein, pp 436-437.)* As a result of the research on the gate control theory of pain, further evidence was gained to conceptualize the pain experience as consisting of three components: sensory-discriminative, motivational-affective, and cognitive-evaluative. The sensory-discriminative component transmits information that tells us where we hurt and what it feels like (e.g., burning, aching, or piercing). The motivational-affective component influences what we do about the pain (e.g., escape, attack, or eradicate its source), and it includes our emotional reaction to the pain. The cognitive-evaluative component determines the meaning of the pain experience to the individual (e.g., the pain of childbirth will have a different meaning than the pain of terminal cancer).

52. The answer is A (1, 2, 3). *(Kandel, ed 2. pp 659-662.)* Even though many sleeping pills are initially helpful, they lose their effectiveness within 2 weeks. The repeated administration of barbiturates (e.g., pentobarbital or phenobarbital) results in a gradual increase in hepatic enzymes, which normally are responsible for the degradation of the barbiturates. Not only is their pharmacological action decreased, but since the liver enzymes are relatively nonspecific, the result is often a broad cross-tolerance to other hypnotics. Barbiturates are known to suppress REM sleep, so that when the drug is withdrawn, a marked REM rebound results, often aggravating insomnia. Even though the benzodiazepines are also addictive, flurazepam increases hepatic enzymes at a much slower rate; hence patients develop a tolerance much more slowly than for pentobarbital. However, an active metabolite of flurazepam remains in the body for a longer period of time (more than 24 hours), resulting in a gradual increase of these breakdown substances in the blood levels. Thus, the effects of the drug are often felt during the daytime as diminished alertness and hand-eye coordination. These symptoms are also aggravated by alcohol.

53. The answer is C (2, 4). *(Iversen, ed 2. pp 151-152.)* The fact that amphetamines act by releasing stored catecholamines such as norepinephrine and dopamine in the brain is demonstrated by the finding that drugs that inhibit catecholamine synthesis also can prevent amphetamine stimulation of behavior. Thus, if catecholamine resynthesis is blocked and its stores are depleted, amphetamines are prevented from exerting their typical effects on behavior.

54. The answer is A (1, 2, 3). *(Iversen, ed 2. pp 171-172.)* Behavioral efficiency is an inverted-U function of arousal or motivational level. Barbiturates tend to stimulate behavior at low doses because of their ability to increase specific arousal by blocking nonsalient stimuli. At high doses, however, these drugs produce nonspecific central nervous system depression, which of course results in reduced arousal and behavioral efficiency.

55. The answer is A (1, 2, 3). *(Kandel, ed 2. p 831.)* In general, there are three ontogenetic stages of synaptic modification. The first is the stage of synapse formation, which occurs under genetic and developmental control. The next stage is that of maintaining the newly developed synapses during early critical periods of development, which requires an appropriate pattern of environmental stimulation. The third stage is the regulation of the transient and long-term effectiveness of the synapses, which takes place throughout life as one initiates and accumulates day-to-day behavioral experience. In effect, environmental and learning factors bring out the latent and potential capabilities for all behaviors by altering the effectiveness of preexisting neural pathways and effecting the expression of new patterns of behavior.

56. The answer is E (all). *(Carlson, ed 3. pp 323-325.)* The physiological responses to dreaming listed in the question can easily be recorded in most people several times a night. If awakened at such times, people confirm that they were dreaming. This complex of physiological signs is commonly referred to as "REM (rapid eye movement) sleep" or "paradoxical sleep." The term "paradoxical sleep" was applied originally because the associated electroencephalographic pattern is characteristic of the alert waking state despite the fact that the dreaming person is, in fact, sound asleep.

57. The answer is C (2, 4). *(Kandel, ed 2. p 831.)* The relationship between social and biological processes has historically been regarded by psychiatry and medicine as organic and functional. Organic mental illnesses have included the dementias and the toxic psychoses. The functional mental illnesses have included the various depressive syndromes, the schizophrenias, and the neuroses. The diseases that produced anatomical evidence of brain lesions were called organic, and those that lacked these features were labeled functional. This distinction should be considered artificial since organic and functional diseases affect mentation and vice versa. In fact, all mental processes are biological and any alteration of these processes is organic. The most significant questions to ask concern the degree to which a biological process is determined by genetic and developmental factors versus toxic or infectious agents versus environmental, social, or behavioral determinants.

58. The answer is A (1, 2, 3). *(Tryon, pp 127-140.)* It has been demonstrated that individuals with a high degree of acquired tolerance are less apt to evidence impairments or exhibit overt signs of intoxication than those who drink socially. Some tolerant individuals can perform psychomotor skills and good mentation with blood alcohol levels between 200 and 300 mg percent. Also, estimates of intoxication based on observations of a drinker's behavior are apt to be invalid. Studies have shown that even trained clinical observers and law enforcement officers make frequent errors in estimating actual levels of intoxication of alcohol abusers. The rate of false-positive errors (i.e., the identification of a sober individual as intoxicated) ranged from 0 to 16.7 percent, while false-negative errors (i.e., failure to identify individuals with positive blood alcohol levels) ranged from 22.2 to 55 percent. Thus, estimation accuracy is extremely variable, with most officers no more accurate than a similarly tested group of social drinkers. Women are more responsive than men to the same dose of alcohol, apparently as a function of hormonal level and stage in the menstrual cycle. Women attain higher blood levels, absorb alcohol faster, and reach peak blood alcohol levels sooner than men; women are even more responsive the day preceding the menstrual cycle and about the time of ovulation.

59. The answer is C (2, 4). *(Lindzey, ed 3. pp 858-859.)* The pathophysiological concomitants that are accompanied by lack of control or uncontrollability of stress result from the activation of the sympathetic adrenal medullary system and the pituitary adrenal cortical axis. There are a number of hormones secreted by the pituitary adrenal system that influence the development of coronary disease and that actually suppress the immune system, rather than activate it. The secretion of corticosteroids is the best example, since they regulate the metabolism of cholesterol and other lipids that participate in the atherosclerotic process. The corticosteroids also have strong immunosuppressive effects. The gastrointestinal system is stimulated by uncontrollable stress, but the result is increased acid secretion, which over time can result in peptic ulcer disease.

60. The answer is B (1, 3). *(Feuerstein, pp 220-221.)* Studies of diabetic patients who practiced progressive muscle relaxation showed significant improvement in glucose tolerance following relaxation training. Relaxation, however, did not affect insulin sensitivity or glucose-stimulated insulin secretory activity. Plasma cortisol levels were reduced in patients trained in relaxation. Thus, stress reduction techniques, such as relaxation, are effective in the management of diabetes.

61. The answer is B (1, 3). *(Carlson, ed 3. pp 334-336.)* Paradoxical sleep is a term given to REM (rapid eye movement) sleep, which is considered paradoxical because its electroencephalographic pattern resembles that of the alert waking state. Dreaming occurs during REM sleep. When an individual is repeatedly awakened during dreaming, a dream deprivation occurs and there is a rebound phenomenon of increased dreaming when the individual is permitted to sleep normally. Dream deprivation does not result in a major decrement in psychological functions (as does sleep deprivation), but it does appear to retard the memory formation of emotionally toned words. While earlier studies suggested the presence of anxiety and irritability, more recent studies have found no such changes in humans even after 16 days of dream sleep deprivation.

62. The answer is A (1, 2, 3). *(Rosen, pp 305-306.)* Of the immunological components that interact with tumor cells, such as T-lymphocytes, macrophages, and humoral antibodies, the natural killer cells show a decrease in activity after psychosocial stress; the most active mechanism is corticosteroid production through the hypothalamic-pituitary-adrenal axis. Natural killer cells play a role in the inhibition of tumor growth and in the surveillance against newly developing primary tumors, at distant sites as well as locally in the body. Recent studies by Glaser, Kiecolt-Glaser, Schleifer, Keller, and others have linked natural killer-cell activity to examination stress, vulnerability to viruses, depression, infectious illness, and bereavement.

63. The answer is A (1, 2, 3). *(Rosen, pp 116-117.)* It has been recognized that exercise decreases the symptoms of hyperglycemia. Under conditions of oral glucose challenge or glucose infusion into the blood stream, physically active persons have an increased rate of glucose removal and a decreased amount of insulin required. Also, the insulin receptors in skeletal muscle and adipose tissue show an increase in sensitivity. Thus, carbohydrate metabolism improves with exercise and physical activity and, within limits, appears to improve with the intensity and duration of the exercise.

64. The answer is C (2, 4). *(Braunwald, ed 11. pp 1241-1243.)* Duodenal ulcer is chronic and recurrent in 6 to 15 percent of the population. It can also exist with or without symptoms. Hence, it is difficult to establish biological and behavioral etiologies. Formerly, an ulcer personality exhibiting oral-receptive characteristics and unmet oral needs was thought to be a dominant factor. While such a personality designation is at best controversial, in general, it has not been substantiated. Psychosocial and behavioral factors, particularly chronic anxiety, psychological stress, cigarette smoking, and diet (including alcohol and coffee), do play a role in the exacerbation of ulcer activity. No difference in frequency of duodenal ulcers has been identified among different socioeconomic classes or occupation groups.

65-69. The answers are: 65-E, 66-B, 67-C, 68-D, 69-A. *(Carlson, ed 3. pp 68-77.)* Acetylcholine is the transmitter agent at the neuromuscular junction. It is released from presynaptic neuron terminals in quantal amounts and excites contractile mechanisms in postsynaptic muscle fibers. Since muscular contractions are the substrate of all behavior patterns, it may be said that acetylcholine is the ultimate mediator of all behavior.

The enzyme dopamine-β-hydroxylase catalyzes the conversion of dopamine to norepinephrine. Evidence suggests that the brains of schizophrenic persons may be deficient in this important enzyme. It is unclear whether this psychopathology results from an accumulation of dopamine or from a relative lack of norepinephrine. Schizophrenia may result in part from the presence of 6-hydroxydopamine in the brain. This substance destroys noradrenergic terminals because of its tendency to form toxic peroxides. In theory, an inborn error of metabolism could produce a high cerebral concentration of 6-hydroxydopamine. Schizophrenia would then occur because of disturbed function in the noradrenergic terminal fields of the brain.

The brain structure most effective in producing positive reinforcement of operant behavior from electric stimulation is the median forebrain bundle. This structure is closely related anatomically and physiologically to the lateral hypothalamic nucleus. The median forebrain bundle contains very high levels of norepinephrine. Apparently, as a neurotransmitter norepinephrine is involved in mediating behavioral reward and motivational processes.

Both dopamine and norepinephrine are capable of functioning as neurotransmitters. Norepinephrine is formed from dopamine in the presence of dopamine-β-hydroxylase. Insofar as norepinephrine may be involved in behavioral reward, its precursor, dopamine, also would be involved.

70-74. The answers are: 70-C, 71-B, 72-B, 73-A, 74-D. *(Williams, RB, pp 3-7, 26-29, 39-43, 88-96.)* Oxytocin and vasopressin are secreted in the supraoptic and paraventricular neurons of the hypothalamus. They are stored in the posterior pituitary where they are excreted into the general circulation. Oxytocin has uterine-contraction and milk-ejection actions. Vasopressin stimulates muscular contraction in the arterioles (raising the blood pressure). It also stimulates contraction of the intestinal musculature, increases peristalsis, and increases concentration of the urine (acting as an antidiuretic). The influences on blood pressure and the intestine are especially relevant for the behavioral sciences.

Follicle-stimulating hormone (FSH) and luteinizing hormone (LH) of the anterior pituitary stimulate the formation of germ cells and the secretion of gonadal hormones. FSH and LH are secreted at a steady level in males. Surges of the hormones underlie the cyclical activities of the female reproductive tract. They can also disrupt development if unbalanced during the critical perinatal period.

Adrenocorticotropic hormone (ACTH) is secreted by the anterior pituitary and has long been associated with the regulation of behavior. It is especially active in response to stressful situations. ACTH and ACTH analogues act directly on the adrenal cortex to stimulate the secretion of corticosteroids in response to stress. They also depress the immune response if taken as a part of a therapeutic regimen or are elevated over an extended period of time.

Corticotropin-releasing hormone (CRH) from the hypothalamus stimulates the secretion of adrenocorticotropic hormone (ACTH) and beta-lipotropin from the pituitary in response to stress. If injected intraventricularly it evokes many of the behavioral and autonomic nervous system reactions normally seen in response to stress. For example, it produces a prolonged increase of plasma norepinephrine, epinephrine, glucagon, glucose, heart rate, and blood pressure, and suppresses gastric acid secretion. Thus, CRH has a direct neurotropic action, activating the sympathetic nervous system and the peripheral catecholamine systems. These are the same systems that are activated under conditions of stress.

Cortisol (hydrocortisone) is secreted by the adrenal cortex in response to anterior pituitary ACTH stimulation. The hypothalamus reacts to various stressors by secreting corticotropin-releasing hormone, which stimulates the anterior pituitary. Increased cortisol release occurs in humans subjected to aversive tasks over which they have little control. It is interesting that humans experiencing bereavement or clinical depression also have cortisol hyperresponsivity. Stress, which can produce adrenal cortical excesses or hyperresponsivity, can influence immunocompetence. It has been suggested that it can promote the development and progression of cancer. Also, adrenergic hyperresponsivity has been found among type A individuals, which, when combined with increased plasma testosterone from threatening and anger-related sensory intake, can contribute to atherogenic processes and coronary artery disease.

75-79. The answers are: 75-A, 76-B, 77-D, 78-C, 79-E. *(Thompson, pp 175-181.)* The barbiturates are sedative hypnotics that act as central nervous system depressants in moderate doses and as anesthetics in higher doses. Barbiturate addiction is common. In fact, compounds in this classification are among the most widely abused drugs in our culture. They tend to be dangerous because their minimum effective dose can be perilously close to the lethal dose. Their effects, moreover, are potentiated by alcohol.

Pentylenetetrazol (Metrazol) is a potent central nervous system stimulant that can lead to tonic-clonic convulsions and death if given in high doses. This drug has been used as a convulsant in conjunction with psychotherapy aimed at relieving acute depressive states. Although the mechanisms by which convulsive therapies relieve depressive symptoms remain a mystery, convulsants continue to be popular adjuncts to traditional psychotherapy.

Cocaine was the first local anesthetic to be discovered (1864). It acts by producing reversible nerve block at the site of application. However, most of its abuse potential derives from central nervous system stimulation. Increasingly popular as a "street drug," cocaine is regarded as potentially dangerous and in some instances addictive.

The well-known stimulant amphetamine is a major drug of abuse in the United States. Widely used for appetite control, amphetamine increases the activity of the biogenic amine norepinephrine by inhibiting monoamine oxidase. Because this enzyme normally breaks down norepinephrine, amphetamine indirectly achieves elevation of norepinephrine levels.

Meprobamate is a mild tranquilizer that produces a pleasant, drowsy state without marked sedative effects. It is commonly prescribed to relieve routine tension and free-floating anxiety. Along with the benzodiazepines, meprobamate is one of the most commonly administered psychotherapeutic agents.

80-85. The answers are: 80-C, 81-A, 82-B, 83-A, 84-D, 85-D. *(Kandel, ed 2. pp 649-654.)* Sleep is a rhythmic and active neural and behavioral process. The sleep-wake cycle is an endogenous rhythm of the body (as are such rhythms as body temperature, urine formation, and cortisol secretion). Human sleep varies from five to seven orderly cycles each night and is characterized by stages 1 through 4 (with increasing slow wave NREM sleep) occurring in the first 30 to 45 minutes, stage 4 being the deepest sleep; the EEG shows that the same stages are then retraced in reverse order. As the stages or depths of sleep increase, the autonomic indicators demonstrate a parasympathetic dominance, with heart rate, blood pressure, and respiration declining and becoming more even, and gastrointestinal mobility increasing. The sleeper is more apt to be awakened spontaneously in stage 1 NREM sleep than in stage 4 NREM sleep.

Stage 1 REM (rapid eye movement) sleep is distinguishable from stage 1 NREM (non-rapid eye movement) sleep by additional electrooculographic and electromyographic criteria. Stage 1 REM sleep is considered to be the dream phase. The first REM sleep period is usually short (5 to 10 minutes), but tends to increase with each successive sleep cycle. Stages 3 and 4 NREM sleep dominate during the first third or half of the night and are less frequent during the later or early morning cycles. Dreams are recalled best when one is awakened from stage 1 REM sleep, and less well during subsequent deeper NREM stages of sleep.

Stage 4 NREM sleep decreases with age and sometimes disappears in persons over 60 years of age. This continuous decline in the elderly is correlated with an increase in the number of spontaneous awakenings. REM sleep and stage 4 NREM sleep are differentially affected by certain psychoactive drugs, especially alcohol and barbiturates, which suppress REM sleep, while stage 4 NREM sleep is especially decreased by the benzodiazepines diazepam (Valium) and chlordiazepoxide (Librium).

Stage 2 NREM sleep increases toward the end of the sleep period and occupies about half of the total sleep time. Dream recall is less if one is awakened during stage 2 NREM sleep than if awakened during stage 1 NREM or stage 1 REM sleep.

86-91. The answers are: 86-E, 87-C, 88-C, 89-A, 90-B, 91-B. *(Tryon, pp 85-100.)* Carbon monoxide produced by smoking behavior is a major health hazard for smokers and nonsmokers. Elevated levels play a role in the etiology of most cardiovascular diseases, including coronary heart disease. It has been associated with peripheral vascular disease, reduced cardiac output, and reduced duration of exercise prior to angina. It also results in decreased oxygen content of fetal blood in a pregnancy as well as subsequent complications in pregnancy. The combination of carbon monoxide and nicotine in smokers contributes to the increased prevalence of fatal and nonfatal cardiovascular disease.

Even though cigarette smoking is by far the major source of exposure to carbon monoxide, occupational exposure (e.g., in blast furnace workers, automobile mechanics, traffic control officers, taxi drivers, truck drivers) as well as urban living and exposure to other people's cigarette smoke can lead to elevated carbon monoxide levels, often with concentrations as high as those of smokers. Other factors affecting one's carbon monoxide level include individual response variability, the way a cigarette is smoked, rate of consumption, the smoker's activity levels, and the variety of tobacco product being smoked. Alcohol consumption will also affect carbon monoxide levels.

Hydrogen cyanide gas is a constituent of cigarette smoke and a primary ciliatoxic agent in cigarette smoking. It is implicated in the development of chronic obstructive pulmonary disease, emphysema, and chronic bronchitis. The combination of hydrogen cyanide gas and carbon monoxide is also implicated in the development of atherosclerosis. Measurement of thiocyanate, the primary metabolite of hydrogen cyanide, serves as an excellent index of smoking behavior and it is also valuable in the discrimination of smokers from nonsmokers. Thiocyanate is also associated with stomach cancer.

Nicotine is inhaled with each puff of cigarette smoke and is now regarded as the major pharmacological addicting agent in smoking. It is absorbed from the lungs so quickly that in only 5 minutes it can be found in the brain, adrenal medulla, and the sympathetic ganglia. Most individuals smoke to obtain pharmacologically satisfying doses of nicotine and they become so accustomed to certain levels of nicotine that they maintain these levels by titrating nicotine intake by adjusting their smoking behavior accordingly. Even though it has central nervous system and cocarcinogenic effects, it primarily acts upon the cardiovascular and respiratory systems. Its deleterious actions on the cardiovascular system include a hemodynamic response of increased work for the heart, increased circulation of fatty acids, and an increase in platelet adhesion and aggregation. While nicotine increases the amount of work of the heart, carbon monoxide reduces the amount of oxygen available to the heart muscle; thus, the combination of carbon monoxide and nicotine links smoking behavior with an increased incidence of atherosclerosis and thrombosis.

92-97. The answers are: 92-E, 93-B, 94-B, 95-D, 96-C, 97-A. *(Williams, RB, pp 3-9, 25-29.)* One of the major advances of recent research has been the revelation of the brain's strong regulatory influence on the endocrine and autonomic nervous systems. This is most relevant when the organism is exposed to changes in its environmental conditions. The more severe the changes, the more severe the stress. The transmission of information in the brain and between the brain and other tissues and systems involves about a dozen amino acids and monoamines. These neurotransmitters function either at the level of the synapse, or as modulators of information flow between neurons. The best-documented neurotransmitters are dopamine, norepinephrine, serotonin, and gamma-aminobutyric acid.

Each neurotransmitter is differentially distributed in the brain for transmission of information from cell to cell. One such system has been referred to as the dopaminergic circuit or system. Parkinson's disease is strongly related to the dopaminergic system. The dopaminergic system is also related to schizophrenia.

The hypothalamic-limbic-midbrain circuits exert a strong regulatory influence on both the endocrine system and the autonomic nervous system. As such, these circuits have a major influence on the cardiovascular and gastrointestinal systems. They also play a major role in mediating the adaptive functions of memory, appraisal, and motivational-emotional responses. Thus, the human neocortex is able to mobilize a metabolic and cardiovascular adaptive response for action by first using these circuits to appraise the functional significance of the environment or of ongoing events. By the brain's maintaining a constant reappraisal from ongoing feedback, these hypothalamic-limbic-midbrain circuits are able to mediate the integrative processes relevant to action or survival.

These circuits are also influenced by neuropeptides (e.g., endorphins, enkephalins, vasopressin). Neuropeptides exist as neurotransmitters and as hormones. By clinging to the nerve cell membrane for varying periods of time, they can modulate the flow of information. Thus, it is believed that the neuropeptides may be able to "fine tune" one's mood.

Psychological stress influences the adrenal cortex and the thyroid. These functional changes occur when one is very upset, anxious, angry, or depressed for a long period of time. In effect, all glands controlled by the anterior pituitary are influenced by a stressful experience.

The hypothalamic hormones influence and coordinate the endocrine system and the autonomic nervous system. They are known as the coordinators of coordinators, since the endocrine system and autonomic nervous system each has major coordinating functions.

98-102. The answers are: 98-C, 99-A, 100-B, 101-D, 102-E. *(Thompson, p 52.)*
Dizygotic (fraternal) twins have similar but not identical genes. The similarity of their genes, however, is not significantly greater than that of other siblings. The fact that the IQs of fraternal twins reared in the same environment are slightly more alike (correlation coefficient: 0.53) than those of other siblings reared in similar circumstances (0.50) must reflect experiential influences on IQ.

The highest correlation between IQ scores is obtained from monozygotic (identical) twins. Identical twins reared together have a correlation coefficient of 0.92; those reared apart, 0.86. This high correlation may be assumed to be a result of both hereditary and environmental factors. In fact, since monozygotic twins have identical genomes, it may be argued that an even higher correlation would exist were it not for the unavoidable factor of slight differences in experience.

The correlation between IQs of siblings reared together (0.50) is higher than that for siblings reared apart (0.42). This observation seems to suggest that environmental factors affect IQ scores considerably. The fact that there is a significant correlation between IQs of siblings reared apart demonstrates the contribution of hereditary factors to intelligence.

A relatively high correlation appears between the IQ scores of siblings reared together. It is much lower, however, than the correlation between dizygotic twins, although their genomes are about equally heterogeneous. This difference is probably attributable to the fact that both society and families tend to treat twins more alike than they do other siblings.

The lowest observed correlation between IQs of offspring occurs for siblings reared apart. However, the correlation is significantly higher than that for unrelated persons who are reared together (correlation factor = 0.25). Thus it seems that hereditary factors are somewhat more potent determinants of IQ than either environmental or experiential factors.

103-110. The answers are: 103-C, 104-A, 105-B, 106-D, 107-B, 108-A, 109-C, 110-E. *(Feuerstein, pp 114-117, 188-189.)* The sympatho-adrenomedullary system increases metabolic activity in response to stressful situations. It generally involves physical exertion. The activity of the sympatho-adrenomedullary system is typically measured by norepinephrine and epinephrine. The system is implicated in such physical disorders as hypertension, atherosclerosis, angina pectoris, cardiac arrhythmias, and myocardial ischemia.

The hypothalamic-pituitary-adrenocortical (HPAC) system responds to emotionally stressful situations in which active coping may not be possible. It also responds to heat, cold, infection, sympathomimetic drugs, and surgery. The system is associated with a "conservation-withdrawal" pattern, characterized by such activities as vigilance, sympathetic nervous system activation, inhibition of movement, and bradycardia associated with the parasympathetic nervous system. Less associated with the "conservation-withdrawal" pattern are various cardiovascular diseases, peptic ulceration, suppression of the immune system, and clinical depression.

The immune system is one of several physiological systems affected by active and passive attempts to cope with stress. Acute stress increases the steroid hormones that are known to be lympholytic, and this response suppresses the immune system. A suppressed immune system increases susceptibility to infection and tumor growth. The immune system is affected by the hypothalamic-pituitary-adrenocortical and central nervous systems.

The endorphin-enkephalin system is involved in aversive situations requiring active coping. It helps reduce fear, inhibit pain-related withdrawal behaviors, and reduce pain during coping responses. These endogenous opiates provide another way for measuring the physiological components of stress.

The anterior hypothalamus when stimulated elicits the relaxation response. Its counterpart, the posterior area of the hypothalamus, stimulates the fight-or-flight reaction. The relaxation response results in hypo- or adynamia of skeletal musculature, decreased blood pressure, decreased respiratory rate, and constricted pupils. These physiological changes are consistent with a generalized decrease in sympathetic activity and are different from changes recorded during quiet sitting or sleep.

Individual Behavior and Personality

DIRECTIONS: Each question below contains five suggested responses. Select the **one best** response to each question.

111. Intelligence quotient (IQ) is given by the relationship between chronologic age (CA) and mental age (MA) expressed as a percentage. The quantitative representation of this relationship is given by which of the following expressions?

(A) $\dfrac{CA}{MA} \times 100$

(B) $\dfrac{CA}{MA} - 100$

(C) $\dfrac{MA}{CA} \times 100$

(D) $\dfrac{MA}{CA} - 100$

(E) $\dfrac{CA}{100} \times MA$

112. Although there is no uniform asthmatic personality type, the most frequent psychological characteristic of boys with bronchial asthma is

(A) hostility
(B) general anxiety
(C) frustrated oral needs
(D) dependency
(E) latent homosexuality

113. Women with rheumatoid arthritis are apt to be characterized by all the following EXCEPT

(A) development of arthritis in the context of stresses associated with demanding and restrictive life events
(B) a family history of mothers who were arbitrary, severe, unreasonable, and controlling
(C) a high degree of covert anger reaction toward their mothers
(D) demonstration of conflicts over the expression of aggressive impulses
(E) reasonable compatibility and comfort with their husbands

114. Essential hypertension has been frequently associated with all the following EXCEPT

(A) repressed anger
(B) acutely stressful events
(C) familial history of hypertension
(D) decreased sympathetic nervous system activity
(E) decreased parasympathetic inhibition

115. The obese individual is overresponsive to all the following cues EXCEPT

(A) gastric contraction
(B) taste
(C) smell
(D) food attractiveness
(E) food abundance

116. In operant conditioning, the rate of extinction is most effectively slowed when the response or learning has been maintained on a reinforcement schedule of

(A) fixed ratio
(B) variable ratio
(C) fixed interval reinforcement
(D) continuous reinforcement
(E) piecework reinforcement

117. According to psychoanalytic theory, which of the following statements about the development of the superego is true?

(A) It is present at birth
(B) It begins to develop during the first 2 years of life
(C) It begins to develop during the fifth or sixth year of life
(D) It begins to develop during puberty
(E) It begins to develop in late adolescence

118. Freud maintained that neuroses were primarily a result of

(A) overly severe toilet training
(B) inappropriate identification
(C) primary processes
(D) inadequate superego development
(E) sexual disturbances

119. Freud maintained that interruptions in the flow of free association were indicative of which of the following?

(A) Reaction formation
(B) Resistance
(C) Repression
(D) Parapraxis
(E) The pleasure principle

120. In traditional psychoanalysis, transference is the process wherein

(A) psychic energy, or libido, is transferred from the id to the ego and superego
(B) a patient invests the analyst with attitudes and feelings derived from vital earlier associations
(C) certain psychological symptoms seemingly defer to new symptoms that frequently are more accessible to analysis
(D) early object choices are gradually decathected
(E) latent dream content is transformed into manifest content

121. The thematic apperception test (TAT) would be most useful for which of the following purposes?

(A) As an aid in differential diagnosis
(B) In prediction of suitability for psychotherapy
(C) In assessment of suicidal risk
(D) In assessment of intellectual level
(E) In assessment of motivational variables

122. All the following are examples of projective tests EXCEPT the

(A) thematic apperception test (TAT)
(B) draw-a-person test
(C) sentence completion test
(D) Rorschach test
(E) Minnesota multiphasic personality inventory (MMPI)

123. In the assessment of personality, the normative and objective method refers to

(A) the use of ''inkblot'' techniques
(B) sophisticated techniques for measuring the accuracy of a person's perception of reality
(C) predictions of behavior on the basis of intensive interviewing
(D) predictions of behavior on the basis of data from personality tests
(E) a way of really evaluating personality rather than of simply assessing how a person behaves

124. Patients suffering from obsessive-compulsive neurosis customarily display which of the following behavior patterns?

(A) Explosive outbursts of temper
(B) Isolation, undoing, and reaction formation
(C) Conversion of psychological conflicts to somatic symptoms
(D) Willingness to engage in antisocial activities and in deviant sexual activity
(E) None of the above

125. All the following statements about schizophrenia are true EXCEPT that

(A) twin, family, and adoption studies have demonstrated that schizophrenia has a significant genetic basis
(B) higher socioeconomic status correlates positively with the incidence of schizophrenia
(C) auditory hallucinations are frequently present
(D) chlorpromazine is an effective form of treatment
(E) communication conflicts in families of schizophrenics play an etiological role

126. Anterograde amnesia is associated with which of the following disorders?

(A) Mild retardation
(B) Hypochondriasis
(C) Sociopathy
(D) Korsakoff's psychosis
(E) Manic-depressive psychosis

127. All the following statements about manic-depressive disorders are true EXCEPT that

(A) the depressive phase is not noticeably different from the disorder of unipolar depression
(B) the manic episodes are of longer duration than are the depressive phases
(C) the suicide risk among manic-depressive patients is greater than that for patients suffering from schizophrenia
(D) the disorder is basically affective and does not involve permanent cognitive deterioration
(E) flight of ideas and euphoria or delusions of grandeur are common symptoms during the manic phase

128. All the following statements about paranoid disorders are true EXCEPT that

(A) denial and projection are the most common defense mechanisms
(B) affected patients characteristically experience high levels of anxiety
(C) hallucinations are frequent, although thinking is rarely delusional
(D) repression of homosexual wishes may be a frequent psychodynamic determinant of the disorder
(E) the prognosis for patients who have classic paranoia is poor

129. A behavior pattern that increases in frequency when followed by a reward is an example of

(A) classical conditioning
(B) shaping
(C) respondent conditioning
(D) operant conditioning
(E) generalization

130. The idea that experimental extinction, which is produced by nonreinforcement after classical conditioning, is an active inhibitory process finds support in the phenomenon of

(A) generalization
(B) spontaneous recovery
(C) experimental neurosis
(D) passive avoidance
(E) active avoidance

131. All the following are tenets of psychoanalytic theory EXCEPT that

(A) all mental events and attitudes have unconscious antecedent causes
(B) a significant portion of the contents of the mind is unconscious
(C) normal and pathological mental functioning are qualitatively different
(D) people strive to maximize pleasure and minimize tension
(E) early experience is important in the formation of individual personality

132. In classical conditioning, the "partial reinforcement effect" is the

(A) inability to learn with fractional reward
(B) increased response retention following partial reinforcement
(C) increased conditioned response amplitudes after nonreinforced trials
(D) reduced response latencies on nonreinforced trials
(E) contrast effects for partial reinforcement schedules

133. A major distinction between the methods for producing classical and instrumental conditioning is that in instrumental conditioning the reinforcing stimulus is

(A) always appetitive in nature
(B) contingent on the behavior to be learned
(C) invariant
(D) solely under the control of the experimenter
(E) unnecessary to produce learning

134. Which of the following type A, or coronary-prone, behavioral factors appears to be the most important?

(A) Hostility
(B) Competitiveness
(C) Time urgency
(D) Explosive speech
(E) Hyperactivity

135. All the following statements about anxiety are true EXCEPT that

(A) intense, manifest anxiety reactions usually involve cardiovascular, respiratory, and gastrointestinal changes
(B) anxiety as subjectively experienced bears no consistent relationship to physiological responses commonly associated with it
(C) anticipation of a stressful event usually reduces the actual level of anxiety the event evokes
(D) all anxiety levels have a negative effect on performance level
(E) avoidance behavior is reinforced when it reduces an anxiety state

136. In Eysenck's theory of personality, the physiological basis of individual differences in the trait dimension of extraversion-introversion is

(A) differential thresholds in the parasympathetic system
(B) differential thresholds in the sympathetic system
(C) differential thresholds in the ascending reticular system
(D) differential lability of the limbic structures
(E) oversecretion or undersecretion of thyrotropic hormone

137. In B. F. Skinner's view, the study of psychology

(A) should be concerned with the fundamental motives that are found in all organisms

(B) should employ factor-analytic procedures to identify the basic dimensions of personality

(C) must be based entirely on an understanding of classical conditioning

(D) cannot make extrapolations about principles of learning from subhuman species to humans

(E) need not make inferences about unobservable organismic states and inner motives

138. Research on rapid eye movement (REM) sleep patterns shows all the following findings EXCEPT that

(A) a newborn baby spends about 50 percent of sleep time in REM sleep

(B) under normal circumstances, 80 percent of the adult sleep cycle consists of REM sleep

(C) deep sleep begins to be replaced with longer periods of REM sleep after the age of 30

(D) the amount of REM sleep determines the amount of actual rest

(E) when REM sleep is interrupted consistently, tiredness and neurotic tendencies develop

DIRECTIONS: Each question below contains four suggested responses of which **one or more** is correct. Select

A	if	**1, 2, and 3**	are correct
B	if	**1 and 3**	are correct
C	if	**2 and 4**	are correct
D	if	**4**	is correct
E	if	**1, 2, 3, and 4**	are correct

139. Self-esteem tends to be positively influenced by

(1) opportunities for favorable social comparison
(2) association with individuals possessing a higher sense of self-worth
(3) feedback of successes and failures in interacting with the environment
(4) sympathetic explanations of continuous negative feedback or comparisons

140. Which of the following will remain fairly constant as one ages between middle and old age?

(1) Emotional stability
(2) Sociability
(3) Assertiveness
(4) Individual personality characteristics

141. In order for operant conditioning to be effectively applied to a psychiatric disorder (e.g., shouting obscenities), one can increase positive, constructive behavior by

(1) precisely defining desired behavior
(2) identifying an effective reinforcer
(3) providing reinforcement when desired behavior is emitted
(4) punishing undesired behavior

142. Factors critical in both classical and operant conditioning include

(1) timing
(2) stimulus discrimination
(3) extinction
(4) simultaneous stimuli

143. The food aversion paradigm is involved in medicine in which of the following?

(1) Chronic alcoholism
(2) Addison's disease
(3) Cancer
(4) Chemotherapy

144. Factors associated with a favorable prognosis in patients who have schizophrenia include

(1) presence of depression or familial history of depression
(2) good premorbid adjustment
(3) a clear precipitating event
(4) a chronic or slow onset of symptoms

145. According to Freud, the superego contains the

(1) conscience
(2) pleasure principle
(3) ego ideal
(4) reality principle

146. The argument that, for purposes of personality assessment, projective techniques are more useful than more objective methods is based on claims that include that projective techniques

(1) are less apt to disclose a tester's purpose
(2) have the benefit of a wealth of normative data
(3) can elicit feelings and thoughts of which a subject may be consciously unaware
(4) have been found to have high reliability and validity

147. Which of the following methods of assessment would be useful in the detection of brain damage?

(1) Thematic apperception test
(2) Bender-Gestalt test
(3) California personality inventory
(4) Rorschach test

148. In Carl Rogers's personality theory, the essential components of a psychotherapeutic process involve

(1) a therapist's unconditional positive regard
(2) a therapist's empathy
(3) reflection of a client's feelings
(4) interpretation of unconscious processes

149. A social learning approach to attitude change includes which of the following methods?

(1) Modeling
(2) Desensitization
(3) Extinction
(4) Direct reinforcement

150. Correct statements regarding systematic desensitization include which of the following?

(1) It was developed by Edward Thorndike of Columbia University
(2) It is used to decrease neurotic anxiety or phobia
(3) Anxiety-provoking situations are brought to mind to be resolved through reality therapy
(4) The patient is taught a technique of muscular relaxation

151. Active versus inactive individuals usually report which of the following psychological factors?

(1) Less depression
(2) More anxiety
(3) More self-confidence
(4) More hostility

152. The type A behavior pattern is characterized by which of the following?

(1) Time urgency
(2) Joyless striving
(3) Hostility
(4) Introspection

153. Which of the following intervention strategies would be effective in changing an individual's type A behavior pattern?

(1) Changing environmental demands
(2) Changing an individual's response to the environment
(3) Changing physiological concomitants of type A behavior
(4) Changing the expectations of the social group or society

SUMMARY OF DIRECTIONS

A	B	C	D	E
1, 2, 3 only	1, 3 only	2, 4 only	4 only	All are correct

154. Posttraumatic stress disorder is characterized by which of the following?

(1) Reexperiencing the event through nightmares
(2) Impulsive or aggressive outbursts of behavior
(3) Apathy, depression, and loss of initiative
(4) Clear and vivid memory

155. The types of validity important in psychological assessment include which of the following?

(1) Incremental
(2) Predictive
(3) Content
(4) Construct

156. The importance of unconscious determinants was strongly emphasized by which of the following personality theorists?

(1) B. F. Skinner
(2) Henry Murray
(3) Kurt Lewin
(4) Sigmund Freud

157. Coping mechanisms differ from defense mechanisms in that they

(1) confront a problem directly and continue to generate possible solutions
(2) get help when one is unable to handle the problem
(3) consciously drop certain habits or form new ones
(4) gather information

DIRECTIONS: Each group of questions below consists of lettered headings followed by a set of numbered items. For each numbered item select the **one** lettered heading with which it is **most** closely associated. Each lettered heading may be used **once, more than once, or not at all.**

Questions 158-160

For each conceptualization of intrinsic motivation, select the investigator with whom it is most closely associated.

(A) Harry Harlow
(B) Wilhelm Wundt
(C) Carl Rogers
(D) David O. Hebb
(E) Jerome Kagan

158. There is a manipulation drive that motivates behavior such as exploration

159. There is an optimal level of physiological arousal such that if arousal is below this level, behavioral responses that increase arousal are reinforced, and if arousal is above this level, arousal-reducing responses are strengthened

160. The reduction of cognitive uncertainty motivates much behavior that is not drive-reducing

Questions 161-163

For each of the following concepts or theoretical constructs, select the worker with whom it is most closely associated

(A) Harry Stack Sullivan
(B) Sigmund Freud
(C) Erik Erikson
(D) Alfred Adler
(E) C. G. Jung

161. Collective unconscious

162. Self-system

163. Postponement of lifetime commitment

Questions 164-166

For each unconscious attitude and conscious attitude that "conceals" it, choose the defense mechanism to which it most closely corresponds.

(A) Reaction formation
(B) Undoing
(C) Denial
(D) Projection
(E) Isolation

164. I hate him (unconscious)—I love him (conscious)

165. I hate him (unconscious)—he hates me (conscious)

166. I hate him (unconscious)—I don't hate him (conscious)

Questions 167-171

For each of the following terms used in psychological assessment, select the evaluative measure with which it is most closely associated.

(A) Bender-Gestalt test
(B) Wechsler adult intelligence scale
(C) Thematic apperception test
(D) Rorschach test
(E) Minnesota multiphasic personality inventory

167. Movement

168. Digit symbol

169. Needs and presses

170. Psychasthenia

171. Lie scale

Questions 172-174

For each therapeutic technique that follows, select the investigator(s) with whom it is most closely associated.

(A) Carl Rogers
(B) Cerletti and Bini
(C) J. L. Moreno
(D) Joseph Wolpe
(E) Leo Kanner

172. Systematic desensitization

173. Client-centered therapy

174. Psychodrama

Questions 175-177

For each phenomenon or diagnostic classification, select the investigator with whom it is most closely associated.

(A) Abraham Maslow
(B) Rene Spitz
(C) B. F. Skinner
(D) Emil Kraepelin
(E) Sergei Korsakoff

175. Disorientation of time and place, irreversible anterograde amnesia, and confabulation or fabrication of the past

176. The classification of schizophrenic psychoses into simple, hebephrenic, catatonic, and paranoid disorders

177. Anaclitic depression, related to early separation from caretakers, in which a child becomes sad, withdrawn, and listless

Questions 178-182

For each schedule of reinforcement, select the response pattern with which it is most closely associated.

(A) Concave-upward scallop
(B) Postreinforcement pause
(C) Stable rates of response and highest resistance to extinction
(D) Smooth, stable rates of response
(E) Satiation and cessation of response

178. Variable ratio

179. Continuous reinforcement

180. Fixed interval

181. Fixed ratio

182. Variable interval

Questions 183-187

For each aspect of personality below select the theorist(s) with whom it is most closely associated.

(A) Carl Rogers
(B) Hans Eysenck
(C) Kurt Lewin
(D) William Sheldon
(E) Miller and Dollard

183. The relationship between temperament and somatotype

184. The discrepancy between self-concept and ideal-self

185. The role of matched-dependent behavior in social learning

186. The role of learning principles and conditioning

187. Behavior as a function of field forces operating in a dynamic life space

DIRECTIONS: Each group of questions below consists of four lettered headings followed by a set of numbered items. For each numbered item select

A	if the item is associated with	(A) **only**
B	if the item is associated with	(B) **only**
C	if the item is associated with	**both** (A) and (B)
D	if the item is associated with	**neither** (A) nor (B)

Each lettered heading may be used **once, more than once, or not at all.**

Questions 188-192

    (A) Classical conditioning
    (B) Operant conditioning
    (C) Both
    (D) Neither

188. An association of a response with a stimulus

189. An association of a conditional and an unconditional stimulus

190. Generally restricted to specific reflex responses that are evoked by specific, identifiable stimuli

191. An increase in the probability of the occurrence of a response after being rewarded

192. A decrease in intensity or probability of a response occurring (extinction or forgetting)

Individual Behavior
and Personality
Answers

111. The answer is C. *(Lerner, 1983. pp 176-177.)* In standard IQ tests such as the Stanford-Binet, mental age is calculated from a test score. A mental age of 9 indicates that test performance was equivalent to that of the average 9-year-old child. If the mental age should be disproportional to the chronologic age, the intelligence quotient correspondingly would be above or below 100. The use of this formula assures that the average score (IQ) will be 100.

112. The answer is D. *(Kaplan, ed 4. pp 512-515.)* Clinical research has determined that the historical formulation of the so-called asthmatic personality is not valid. Psychological factors are important, however, and it has been determined that about one-half of the patients with asthma have strong unconscious wishes for protection centering on individuals on whom they are dependent. Threat of loss or separation from the mother can produce attacks of bronchial asthma in some individuals, whereas in others the wish for protection produces an intense conflict, so that separation can actually produce a remission from an attack. Asthmatic boys, rather than girls, tend to be more dependent on their mothers, whereas asthmatic girls tend to be more dependent on their fathers. Although girls may try to be self-sufficient, they are frequently chronically depressed. Boys are also apt to be passively dependent, timid, and immature. Both, however, appear to be dominated by a fear of losing parental support. Studies have found that about 50 percent of all asthmatic attacks, regardless of a patient's age at the time of occurrence, are initiated or precipitated by actual or anticipated separation from or loss of the person on whom he or she is dependent.

113. The answer is E. *(Kaplan, ed 4. pp 527-529.)* While there may be a genetic predisposition for rheumatoid arthritis, psychosocial factors can lead to the precipitation of the disease and its exacerbations. The illness tends to develop in the context of life events that are demanding and restricting. Women are three times as likely as men to develop rheumatoid arthritis, and studies of their backgrounds show that their mothers are recalled as being arbitrary, severe, unreasonable, and controlling. Arthritic women also have a high degree of covert anger and exhibit conflicts over expression of aggressive impulses and anger. They show high status stress and high discrepancy between their own and their husbands' status variables. Rheumatoid arthritic women and their husbands tend to express a great deal of anger and hostility toward each other. Their husbands are more likely to have peptic ulcers.

114. The answer is D. *(Hamburg, pp 126-129.)* One of the earliest psychosocial hypotheses on the etiology of hypertension was that it was anger directed inward because of an inability to express anger properly. While it has been demonstrated that hypertensives do tend to avoid involvement and confrontation, additional relevant factors are involved. Acutely stressful events have been related to hypertension, and it has been demonstrated that individuals with a familial history of hypertension have an increased response to environmental and behavioral stressors compared with normotensive controls. Increased sympathetic nervous system activity and diminished parasympathetic inhibition result in increased blood pressure, which suggests a possible disturbance of central autonomic regulation with possible increased sensitivity to stressors.

115. The answer is A. *(Braunwald, ed 11. p 1675.)* Many studies have shown that obese individuals respond less well than normal individuals to internal cues, such as gastric contraction. They also overrespond to external cues such as taste, smell, food attractiveness, food abundance, and ease of obtaining food. This is significant because behavior modification can be used to influence eating behaviors by changing the exposure to and pattern and nature of the external cues. Since behavior patterns are learned, they can be changed or unlearned.

116. The answer is B. *(Kandel, ed 2. p 87.)* Extinction is the gradual reduction of a conditioned response, usually the result of withholding or altering the reinforcement or reward. Extinction is slowed when reinforcement occurs on a variable schedule (i.e., not every response being rewarded) rather than a continuous reinforcement schedule (every response rewarded). Gambling behavior, for example, is maintained powerfully through variable ratio reinforcement, even when there are long periods of nonreinforced responses. A fixed ratio schedule would provide a reinforcement after a specific number of responses or objects were produced (e.g., in a factory worker's schedule). In a fixed interval schedule, a person is reinforced only after a certain time has elapsed, such as with a monthly salary check. Piecework reinforcement is similar to a fixed ratio schedule with a reward being provided after each piece of work is produced.

117. The answer is C. *(Brenner, pp 113-114, 122-124.)* Freud maintained that the superego begins to develop around the age of 5 or 6 as part of the resolution of the Oedipus complex. At the end of the phallic stage of psychosexual development (which lasts from around 2½ to 6 years of age), children must abandon the sexual and aggressive impulses that were directed toward their parents in order to avoid the parents' strong disapproval. In abandoning these impulses, children identify with their parents. Part of this identification involves the internalization of parental standards of morality; this internalization marks the beginning of the superego.

118. The answer is E. *(Lerner, 1983. pp 64-70.)* Although Freud modified many aspects of his theory of neuroses, he never wavered in his conviction that sexual disturbances were the most important causal factor in neurotic development. One of the first to recognize the existence of sexual feelings and curiosity in children, Freud maintained that in the course of socialization some of a child's sexual feelings become repressed. Occasionally, the act of repression reaches extreme proportions, consuming enormous amounts of psychic energy. Under stress, this repression often would fail, allowing the sexual impulses, partially freed, to appear in the form of neurotic symptoms.

119. The answer is B. *(Lerner, 1986. pp 511-513.)* One of the most important techniques in psychoanalysis is free association, in which a patient is encouraged to say whatever comes to mind, however absurd or objectionable it might seem. This can be a difficult undertaking; frequently, the flow of associations is interrupted and a patient's train of thought is blocked or lost because of resistance, a defensive maneuver that prevents repressed material from emerging into consciousness.

120. The answer is B. *(Mischel, ed 4. p 82.)* In traditional psychoanalytic treatment, analysts purposely reveal very little about themselves to their patients. That is intended to help promote transference—that is, to create an ambiance that facilitates a patient's ability to transfer his or her past emotional attachments to the psychoanalyst. The analyst becomes a substitute for the parental figure. In positive transference, the patient becomes attached to the analyst in order to obtain love and emotional satisfaction, whereas in negative transference the analyst is seen as an unfair, unloving, and rejecting parental figure. Interpretations of transference may help the patient see the positive or negative feelings as a reflection of previous emotional entanglements.

121. The answer is E. *(Kaplan, ed 4. pp 32, 129-130, 707.)* The thematic apperception test (TAT), which consists of a series of 30 ambiguous pictures about which subjects are asked to construct a story, is most useful in assessing motivational variables. It provides a case-study exploration of an individual's personality. Although it also has been employed to assess variables such as intellectual level, other tests are more suitable for such purposes (e.g., IQ tests). The TAT is not particularly helpful in differential diagnosis.

122. The answer is E. *(Anastasi, ed 5. pp 500-507, 564-591.)* Projective methods of personality assessment comprise those measures that are relatively unstructured and have no correct answers. Subjects' responses to such measures are presumed to be more indicative of individual characteristics than is the case with more structured tests, responses to which are inclined to be determined more by the nature of the test than of the subject taking it. The thematic apperception test, draw-a-person test, sentence completion test, and Rorschach test are all considered to be projective methods of measurement. The Minnesota multiphasic personality inventory (MMPI) is a structured personality inventory of 550 items that must be answered "True," "False," or "Cannot Say."

123. The answer is D. *(Kaplan, ed 4. pp 126-132.)* Normative and objective methods involve statistical prediction based on quantified data. Applied to the assessment of personality, such methods are independent of any particular theory of personality, relying on the use of a mathematical relationship between relevant test scores and a particular behavioral outcome that is to be predicted. The 1950s and 1960s witnessed a controversy over the relative merits of personality assessment and prediction on the basis of clinical interviewing techniques versus those of actuarial and statistical data; today, researchers and clinicians usually do not view these procedures as incompatible, and both methods currently are employed for different types of research or personality assessment.

124. The answer is B. *(Sarason, ed 4. p 170.)* The rigid defensive style characteristic of persons who have obsessive-compulsive neurosis is accomplished by the mechanisms of isolation, undoing, and reaction formation. Isolation is the exclusion of an event from the continuum of meaningful experience; for example, an idea or action may be separated from its original emotional content. Undoing connotes the repetitious patterns of ideation and behavior that are typical of obsessive rituals; an affected patient may feel compelled to undertake an action that counteracts an idea that has recently been expressed or an event that has just occurred. Reaction formation refers to the way in which obsessive-compulsive patients attempt to control an unacceptable wish by undertaking an exaggerated opposing action; kindly actions, for example, may be a reaction against sadistic wishes.

125. The answer is B. *(Braunwald, ed 11. pp 2093-2096.)* Schizophrenia is a serious mental disorder with about 1 percent prevalence across all cultures. It has a 6-month or longer duration and causes significant social, occupational, and personal disability and suffering. Diagnosis includes at least 6 months of bizarre delusions often with persecutory or jealous content, auditory hallucinations, and grossly disorganized behavior. The most significant etiological factor is genetic as confirmed by twin, family, and adoption studies. There is a higher incidence in persons of lower socioeconomic status, but it is difficult to determine whether this is because of a "social drift" of more vulnerable individuals or the stresses of lower socioeconomic status, especially in genetically vulnerable individuals. A major psychosocial factor is a frequent pattern of communication conflicts between parents and between parents and the child or developing adult. There is also a stress-diathesis model whereby predisposed individuals are vulnerable to certain stressful circumstances. The phenothiazines are the most effective form of chemical treatment.

126. The answer is D. *(Suinn, p 275.)* The characteristic symptoms of Korsakoff's psychosis are disorientation in time and place, confabulation, and anterograde amnesia. Anterograde amnesia is a specific cognitive deficit in which events that have just occurred are not recalled. Affected patients typically fabricate responses to questions about the forgotten occurrences. Inadequate nutritional habits (specifically, vitamin B deficiency) are the probable cause of Korsakoff's psychosis; hence the disorder frequently is associated with a history of chronic alcoholism.

127. The answer is B. *(Suinn, pp 354-363.)* Manic-depressive disorders involve recurrent affective disturbances alternating between manic and depressive periods. Characteristically, the manic phase is much shorter than the depressive phase; whereas the mania may last from a matter of days or weeks to 3 or 4 months, the depression lasts 9 months or more. Many clinicians now believe that such mood swings can be effectively controlled by lithium carbonate. Chromosome 11 has recently been demonstrated to be involved.

128. The answer is C. *(Suinn, pp 400-405.)* Although hallucinations are not unknown in paranoid disorders, they are very infrequent. Such disorders usually are identified by markedly delusional thinking of a persecutory, grandiose, or jealous character. Cognitive functioning in paranoid disorders generally is not grossly impaired except in relation to the subject matter of the delusional symptoms.

129. The answer is D. *(Schneiderman, pp 162-163.)* The influence of behavior by rewards and punishments has its roots in classical studies of learning. In the earlier classical conditioning experiments, Pavlov investigated the acquired associations between environmental stimuli (food, bell) and smooth muscle responses (salivation). By pairing the food and bell he elicited salivation using only the bell. This is known as generalization of a response to two or more stimuli. In operant conditioning, the desired behavior is rewarded or reinforced with an object, food, praise, or other reward of pleasing consequence to the learner. Shaping involves rewarding the person's behavior as it begins to approach or approximate the desired or ideal behavior until the desired behavior is reached or mastered. The therapeutic use of this ability to increase or control certain behaviors by reinforcing the desired behavior is the essence of behavioral modification. Behavioral modification has repeatedly demonstrated its efficacy in changing behavior and establishing ''good'' behaviors in such areas as self-care, social behavior, psychiatric pathology, eating behaviors, smoking, and pain.

130. The answer is B. *(Hall, JF, pp 28-29.)* Spontaneous recovery, first described by Pavlov, is the return of response strength in due course after extinction. If extinction produced forgetting, then presumably the loss of responsiveness would be permanent. Return of the previously learned material suggests that it is not lost but rather suppressed by some active process resulting from nonreinforcement. Additional support for this concept comes from the finding that responses may return at full strength following a single reinforcement at the end of extinction.

131. The answer is C. *(Brenner, pp 179-180.)* Before the development of psychoanalytic theory, psychopathological manifestations were considered to be evidence of mental disorders having nothing in common with normal mental functioning. One of Freud's greatest contributions lay in his recognition that identical psychological processes operate in both normal and abnormal mental functioning, i.e., that any differences between normality and abnormality are quantitative, not qualitative. The necessary implication of Freud's perception is that any judgments as to a person's "normality" are relative and that there are no clear criteria by which a person can be classified as psychologically ill.

132. The answer is B. *(Hall, JF, p 133.)* The retarded rate of extinction following partial reinforcement in acquisition was labeled the "partial reinforcement effect" by Lloyd Humphreys (1939). This consistent effect was regarded as something of a paradox since resistance to extinction was thought to be a function of response strength built up by reinforcement during training. According to this reasoning, partial reinforcement should produce faster, not slower, extinction.

133. The answer is B. *(Hall, JF, p 184.)* A contingency relationship between response and reinforcement is characteristic of instrumental conditioning. For this form of learning, reinforcement occurs only if the desired response is emitted. Therefore, the occurrence of reinforcement is at least partly under the control of the learner.

134. The answer is A. *(Weiss, 1984. pp 44-45.)* Among the psychosocial variables considered to be risk factors for coronary heart disease, the type A, or coronary-prone, behavior pattern is most prominent. The type A behavior pattern consists of extremes of competitiveness, a chronic sense of time urgency, easily evoked hostility, aggressiveness, explosive speech, and increased rate of activity. More recent studies have shown that aggressiveness and hostility (especially unexpressed hostility) are the most consistent and important factors.

135. The answer is D. *(Mischel, ed 4. pp 396-404.)* There is no simple linear relationship between task performance and level of arousal or anxiety. The Yerkes-Dodson theory posits a curvilinear relationship between these variables in which performance is enhanced at a certain optimal level of arousal; anxiety levels lower or higher than this optimum have a detrimental effect on performance. There is evidence in support of the Yerkes-Dodson formulation. It also has been demonstrated that such factors as task complexity, instructional set, and intelligence alter the quantitative features of the curvilinear relationship between performance and anxiety.

136. The answer is C. *(Eysenck, pp 12-21.)* H. J. Eysenck's factor-analytic study of personality identifies two major trait dimensions, extraversion-introversion and neuroticism-stability. These dimensions may be assessed by objective tests and are predictive of behavior in a range of situations. Eysenck hypothesizes that individual differences in these dimensions are based on physiological substrates. He believes that neuroticism is related to a general factor of limbic lability (neurotic persons having highly labile limbic structures) and that extraversion-introversion is related to differential thresholds of the ascending reticular formation (extraverted persons having weak arousal and rapid attenuation of incoming stimulation).

137. The answer is E. *(Mischel, ed 4. pp 282-291.)* B. F. Skinner's radical behaviorist approach to psychology is based on the idea that behavioral science should restrict itself to the recording and analysis of observable behavioral responses. Skinner argues that it is unnecessary to make inferences about such inner states as arousal, need levels, motives, and cognitions. Skinner analyzes behavior in terms of the principles of classic Pavlovian conditioning and, more importantly, operant learning. Operant learning (instrumental conditioning) involves changing the relationship between reinforcement schedules and response outcomes.

138. The answer is B. *(Kolb, ed 2. pp 268-270.)* Sleep is divided into two distinct states: D-sleep (desynchronized EEG pattern sleep) and S-sleep (synchronized EEG pattern sleep). D-sleep is also known as REM (rapid eye movement) or dreaming sleep; S-sleep as NREM (non-rapid eye movement), orthodox, or quiet sleep. D and REM sleep are used interchangeably, as are S and NREM sleep. S-sleep (NREM) is divided into stages 1, 2, 3, and 4, with stage 1 being the lightest and stage 4 the deepest. NREM sleep lasts from 60 to 100 minutes, followed by 10 to 40 minutes of REM sleep, and the cycle is continued throughout the night. Typically, about 80 percent of an adult's sleep time is spent in NREM sleep and 20 percent in REM sleep. REM sleep tends to increase during the second half of the night. The amount of REM sleep appears to determine the amount of rest. When REM sleep is interrupted, tiredness tends to develop. A newborn spends about 50 percent of sleep time in REM sleep. Deep sleep begins to be replaced by longer periods of lighter sleep after the age of 30.

139. The answer is B (1, 3). *(Lindzey, ed 3. pp 852-855.)* Self-esteem can be enhanced or reduced by several social and psychological processes. Self-esteem is generally not influenced by normative factors and not transmitted or affected by association with individuals possessing a higher sense of self-worth. The most effective process is for the individual to actively engage in favorable social comparison actions and receive feedback on successes and failures in interacting with the environment. These comparisons and feedback cannot be continuously negative, even though they are accompanied by sympathetic support and explanations. Individuals who are exposed to large threats to self-esteem of long duration are especially vulnerable.

140. The answer is E (all). *(Andres, pp 141-143.)* Theorists have postulated that the universal processes of aging include the decline of emotionality, the reversal of sex-role-linked characteristics, and the development of wisdom. Longitudinal studies, however, have shown that an individual's personality shows little or no change with age. There is little or no change in traits such as emotional stability, sociability, assertiveness, and other characteristics of the individual personality. In other words, a 40-year-old who is well adjusted, assertive, and liberal is apt to be a well-adjusted, assertive, liberal 80-year-old; likewise, a 40-year-old person who is neurotic and selfish is apt to be a neurotic and selfish 80-year-old. Thus, personality is considered to be relatively stable over the life span.

141. The answer is A (1, 2, 3). *(Kandel, ed 2. pp 809-810.)* Specific behavioral problems, such as shouting obscenities, messiness, or poor hygenic habits, that are often found in institutionalized psychiatric patients can be reduced and replaced with positive and constructive behavior through operant reinforcement by first precisely defining the behavior to be established, then finding an effective reinforcement (e.g., praise, attention, compliments, privileges, money, tokens, food), and finally training the staff to provide the appropriate reinforcement when the desired behavior is emitted by the patient. Punishment is not usually a part of operant reinforcement if one wishes to establish positive and constructive behavior.

142. The answer is A (1, 2, 3). *(Kandel, ed 2. pp 808-809.)* Timing is critical in both classical and operant conditioning. In classical conditioning, the conditional stimulus and unconditional stimulus must be presented closely, otherwise learning is poor or slow. In operant conditioning, the reinforcer must follow the desired response without delay, or only weak conditioning will occur. The individual or animal must be able to discriminate between the two stimuli (stimuli discrimination) in classical conditioning in order for the second stimulus to be able to elicit the response. Extinction occurs in classical conditioning if the conditional stimulus is repeatedly presented without the unconditional stimulus. Likewise, if reinforcement is not given when the desired response occurs in operant conditioning, the probability of the response occurring decreases until the response eventually ceases. Simultaneous stimuli presentation is relevant for classical conditioning, but not necessary for operant conditioning.

143. The answer is E (all). *(Kandel, ed 2. p 809.)* Food aversion (also called bait shyness in animals) is a basic biological process in which persons learn to avoid poisoned substances. The person develops an aversion to food that is followed by nausea produced by a poison. The food aversion paradigm has been applied to the treatment of chronic alcoholism when alcohol is followed by a powerful emetic such as apomorphine. The same mechanism appears to be involved when a person with Addison's disease becomes conditioned to avoid diets deficient in salt and diets that produce malaise. Certain forms of cancer also produce malaise that induces food aversion and depressed appetite. The nausea following chemotherapy for cancer also produces an aversion to foods tasted before the treatment.

144. The answer is A (1, 2, 3). *(Suinn, pp 400-401.)* Considerable attention has been directed toward identifying favorable prognostic indicators in schizophrenia. Those factors most frequently associated with favorable signs for recovery are the acute onset of symptoms, a clear precipitating event, good premorbid adjustment, presence of confusion and disorientation, and the presence of depression or familial history of depression. The presence of these factors is associated with briefer hospitalization and with a lower relapse rate.

145. The answer is B (1, 3). *(Hall, CS, pp 38-39.)* According to Freud, the superego is composed of two subsystems, the conscience and the ego ideal. The conscience refers to the set of internalized moral prohibitions that guides personal behavior. The ego ideal is the set of positive values and standards of correct behavior that a child internalizes and that the ego tries to emulate.

146. The answer is B (1, 3). *(Anastasi, ed 5. pp 564-591.)* Proponents of projective methods of personality assessment argue that because the stimuli involved usually are relatively ambiguous and the task is unstructured, subjects are less aware of what a tester is looking for and hence more free to provide an unfettered response than is the case with more objective methods. It also is argued that because of their unstructured nature, projective techniques are less apt to provoke defensive reactions and more apt to encourage fantasy and therefore more likely to produce unconscious material. However, there is general agreement that a serious limitation of projective methods is the lack of adequate normative data, leaving interpretation by and large up to individual clinicians. Above all, the reliability and validity of projective techniques are difficult to assess; despite many attempts, such assessments have proved inconclusive.

147. The answer is C (2, 4). *(Kaplan, ed 4. pp 126-136.)* Both the Rorschach and the Bender-Gestalt tests can be useful in the assessment of brain damage. Various atypical responses to the Rorschach cards (e.g., poor form responses) have been found to be related to brain damage. The Bender-Gestalt test consists of eight test figures that a subject is asked to copy; difficulties in this easy task often are indicative of brain dysfunction. Neither the thematic apperception test nor the California personality inventory has been found to be a sensitive indicator of cerebral damage.

148. The answer is A (1, 2, 3). *(Lerner, 1986. pp 418-419, 514-516.)* Carl Rogers's formulation of client-centered therapy requires that therapists establish an atmosphere of empathic understanding and of unconditional positive regard for their clients by communicating to them that they are liked and respected whatever they may say or do. Once this atmosphere is established, Rogers's main therapeutic technique is to reflect clients' feelings back to themselves. Rogers feels that this helps them to clarify feelings and attitudes that are conflictive or otherwise difficult. He further argues that a client-centered therapist should not offer interpretations of behavior, attitudes, or unconscious wishes.

149. The answer is E (all). *(Lerner, 1986. pp 419-425.)* Social learning theory suggests that all the following are methods of attitude change: direct reinforcement—rewarding an expression of the desired attitude or behavior; extinction—denying the rewards that maintain the attitude that is to be changed; and modeling—watching someone else being rewarded for desired responses and punished for undesired ones. Desensitization is a technique for conditioning neutral or positive responses to previously fear-inducing stimuli. It, too, is based on social learning principles.

150. The answer is C (2, 4). *(Kandel, ed 2. pp 808-809.)* Systematic desensitization was developed by Joseph Wolpe in an effort to decrease neurotic anxiety or phobias that are usually precipitated by certain environmental situations, such as fear of heights or crowds. The patient is taught muscular relaxation; then, while using the relaxation to inhibit the anxiety, the patient is told to imagine a series of progressively more severe anxiety-provoking situations (e.g., climbing to the second step of a ladder, then the fourth step, and so on) until the anxiety-provoking situation of the highest (strongest) level can be brought to mind without the accompanying anxiety or fear. The anxiety-provoking situation is not brought to mind to be treated by any special form of psychotherapy, but becomes paired with the anxiety-reducing relaxation. Most of these anxiety-provoking situations are situation-specific; however, the desensitization often generalizes to other real-life situations that may be potentially anxiety-provoking. Edward Thorndike introduced the major paradigm of associational learning called operant, or instrumental, conditioning.

151. The answer is B (1, 3). *(Rosen, pp 119-120.)* Studies of males involved in aerobic-type exercise and jogging have reported a significant reduction in anxiety, depression, and hostility when these males are compared with sedentary controls. They have also reported greater self-confidence. Type A males also showed a reduction in type A behavior patterns. Biological stress-reducing factors that could influence such psychological factors are the usual reduction of circulating catecholamines and the increase in beta-endorphins occurring during exercise.

152. The answer is A (1, 2, 3). *(Rosen, pp 131-133.)* The type A behavior pattern is exhibited by individuals who are particularly prone to ischemic heart disease. It is characterized by time urgency, joyless striving, and hostility. Introspection is infrequent since the individual is so hard-driving, striving, and impatient that stopping and looking inward is not tolerated except to criticize and chastise oneself for minor errors and lack of achievement.

153. The answer is A (1, 2, 3). *(Rosen, pp 134-140.)* In general, there are three major interactive strategies used in attempting to intervene and change type A behavior patterns: changing the environmental demands, changing an individual's responses to the environment (both behavioral and cognitive), and changing the physiological concomitants of type A behaviors. Examples of counteracting certain environmental demands or triggers include limiting time spent in the environment, rescheduling deadlines, or avoiding interruptions. Changing one's response is best accomplished by learning to observe one's own type A behaviors and then contracting with oneself to alter those behaviors by practicing new behaviors, coping styles, or reactions. Progressive relaxation, biofeedback, and exercising are effective methods of reducing many of the physiological responses to stress and anxiety. Attempting to change the expectations of a social group or society is very difficult, especially if the changes are to be directed at one's own personal needs.

154. The answer is A (1, 2, 3). *(Suinn, pp 143-149.)* Posttraumatic stress disorder is clearly linked to a traumatic event, such as a natural disaster, accidental disaster, or warfare. Physicians should be alert to anxiety symptoms that can follow such catastrophes. They may include reexperiencing the trauma through nightmares or reliving the event, emotional numbness, exaggerated startle response, inability to fall asleep, apathy or depression, apprehension, tremors, poor concentration, poor memory following the event, and impulsive or aggressive outbursts of behavior. The individual is so overwhelmed that there is a breakdown of normal coping patterns and a physiological strain imposed on the person. Early treatment is crucial and consists of the prevention of the patient's refuge in escape, the reassurance that complete breakdown has not occurred, and the physician's acceptance of the patient's fear and exhaustion. Prevention includes emphasizing to physicians the reactions to expect of victims of various ages.

155. The answer is E (all). *(Lanyon, ed 2. pp 148-158.)* Incremental, predictive, content, and construct validity all are important in composing psychological assessment techniques. Incremental validity refers to the extent to which a test or test items significantly add to information obtained from prior tests or test items. Predictive validity means the extent to which an assessment technique allows the person using it to predict a future behavior or test score. Content validity involves showing that the content of the test is representative of the behaviors of interest to the investigator. Finally, construct validity demonstrates whether a technique can be shown to relate in theoretically understandable ways to other relevant tests and measures.

156. The answer is C (2, 4). *(Hall, CS, pp 681-705.)* Although Sigmund Freud is best known for the development of the theory of the unconscious, Henry Murray also strongly emphasized the unconscious in the development of his theory of personality. Both Freud and Murray constructed a system of human needs and wishes that existed in the unconscious part of the mind. According to the theory, these unconscious needs and wishes express themselves through the personality of the individual and exert considerable influence on individual behavior. Freud arrived at his discovery through the observation of his patients and the analysis of his own dreams, from which he developed his technique of dream analysis. Murray applied the concept of the unconscious in his theory of personality. He is best known for his development of the thematic apperception test, which utilizes a projective technique to elicit personal and interpersonal conflicts, needs, and attitudes. Carl Jung also placed a strong emphasis on unconscious factors in personality.

B. F. Skinner and Kurt Lewin deemphasized the unconscious in the normal personality. Skinner provided experimental analyses of operant behavior to demonstrate that personality is the result of reinforcement and conditioning. Lewin constructed a field theory of action and emotion modeled on physical theory and topology.

157. The answer is E (all). *(Brophy, pp 223-225.)* Coping mechanisms are actions that resolve conflicts in socially or personally desirable and effective ways. Conflicts are often the results of inconsistencies that exist in our behaviors, our cognitions, or between conflicting cognitions and behaviors. If we are capable of coping, we take action to resolve the problem as well as we can and see that it does not occur again. For example, if there is a conflict between two behaviors, resolution may require considering the behaviors in relationship to our ideals and then changing one or both of them. Or, if the conflict is between two cognitions, we may need to seek information, then pursue changing one or both of the cognitions. If the conflict is between cognition and behavior, then we generally attempt to change either or both to make one conform with the other. Thus coping involves a resolution of the conflict achieved by changing one or both of the conflicting elements. This is not to be confused with the use of defense mechanisms to resolve conflicts. Although defense mechanisms can be appropriate or at least preferable to other available alternatives, they generally ''defend'' us and do not generally change behavior or resolve the conflict itself. Coping mechanisms confront the problem directly, continue to generate possible solutions, generate more information, get help when needed, and allow us consciously to drop certain habits or form new ones. Coping mechanisms allow us to take action to eliminate the undesirable cognition or behavior causing the conflict, whereas defense mechanisms most often remove awareness of the conflict, allow the conflicting elements to continue, and provide an illusion of solution; but the problem continues.

158-160. The answers are: 158-A, 159-D, 160-E. *(Deci, pp 11-40.)* The evidence for kinds of behavior that are not motivated by their drive-reducing or need-fulfilling properties has generated a long-standing theoretical controversy. One of the earliest explanations for such behavior was the postulation of a stimulation-seeking drive. This drive has been variously called an exploratory drive (K. C. Montgomery), a drive to avoid boredom (A. K. Meyers and Neal Miller), or a manipulation drive (Harry Harlow). These motivational postulates have been criticized as mere labels that fail to provide an understanding of how such drives operate. Much recent work in this field has focused on the role of discrepancy or incongruity in intrinsic motivation.

David O. Hebb supplies an alternative theory of drive motivation based on the hypothesis of an optimal level of arousal. This hypothesis implies that behavior is reinforced to the extent that it contributes to the maintenance of this optimal level.

Jerome Kagan offers a more cognitive solution, arguing that uncertainty is a dystonic state, the reduction of which is a motivating force. In this view, uncertainty is the result of an incompatibility or incongruity between a cognitive structure and another structure, experience, or behavior.

161-163. The answers are: 161-E, 162-A, 163-C. *(Erikson, pp 156-158. Hall, CS, pp 116-117, 184-186.)* C. G. Jung believed that every person inherits the potential to experience and recall memories and images from humanity's evolutionary past. Referring to these predispositions as the collective unconscious, Jung considered this to be one of the most powerful components of the mind, especially in persons who suffer psychological illness.

Harry Stack Sullivan coined the term self-system to describe the series of behavioral controls and defensive operations that a person adopts in order to avoid the disruptive effects of anxiety. Sullivan felt that the more anxiety a person has experienced, the more active role the self-system plays in that person's personality. Indeed, the self-system can assume such dominance that, in attempting to ward off anxiety, it interferes with an affected individual's perception of reality and hence with the ability to function adaptively.

Erik Erikson's idea of the psychosocial moratorium describes the prolonged adolescence characterizing modern American culture, an adolescence that allows persons in their late teens or twenties to postpone lifetime commitments such as marriage and definite careers. During this moratorium, individuals can experiment with various life-styles and career possibilities. Erikson believes that this moratorium serves a very positive function in society.

164-166. The answers are: 164-A, 165-D, 166-C. *(Brenner, pp 84-100.)* Reaction formation is the defensive process whereby an unacceptable feeling or impulse is converted into, and consciously experienced as, its opposite. Thus, in reaction formation, "I hate him" becomes "I love him."

Projection is the process through which unacceptable impulses are at once denied and attributed to someone else or to something in the environment. Thus, in projection, "I hate him" is converted into "he hates me."

Denial is the defense mechanism by means of which any aspect of reality, e.g., forbidden thoughts, is actively denied. With this defense mechanism, "I hate him" becomes "I don't hate him."

The defense mechanism of undoing refers to an action that is meant somehow to reverse or "undo" the damage that is felt to have been caused by an unacceptable wish.

Isolation is the conscious experience of an unacceptable wish or thought without the painful effect associated with it. Isolation and undoing both are defenses characteristic of people who have obsessive-compulsive personality styles.

167-171. The answers are: 167-D, 168-B, 169-C, 170-E, 171-E. *(Kaplan, ed 4. pp 126-136.)* Movement scores can be obtained on the Rorschach test. The movement score is the number of times a subject perceives motion in the inkblots. Three types of movement responses are scored on the Rorschach: human movement (M), animal movement (FM), and inanimate movement (m). Human movement responses are felt to reflect the extent to which subjects are able to exercise their imaginative capacities. Animal movement responses often are interpreted as representing the extent to which subjects are aware of their impulses toward immediate gratification. Inanimate movement responses are thought to be indicators of internal tension and of feeling subject to forces outside one's control.

Digit symbol is the name of one of the performance subtests of the Wechsler adult intelligence scale. In this subtest, nine numbers are paired with nine symbols, and subjects are presented with several rows of numbers and given a specified amount of time in which to translate as many numbers into symbols as they can. This subtest was designed to assess psychomotor speed.

The thematic apperception test (TAT) was designed by Henry A. Murray to analyze a subject's needs and presses (environmental forces acting on an individual). This test consists of a series of pictures; for example, one picture depicts a boy staring at a violin. These pictures are shown to subjects who are asked to make up a story about each. The TAT is perhaps most useful in assessing motivational variables.

The Minnesota multiphasic personality inventory (MMPI) contains both a psychasthenia (Pt) and a lie scale. The former appears to be most closely associated with obsessive-compulsive manifestations. The lie scale is a score based on MMPI items that, when answered in a certain way, are socially desirable but usually not true. This scale was added to the MMPI in an attempt to detect persons who were attempting to present themselves in a "good" light.

172-174. The answers are: 172-D, 173-A, 174-C. *(Davison, ed 4. pp 485-489, 498-503, 528-529.)* The technique of systematic desensitization was developed by Joseph Wolpe during the 1950s on the basis of pioneering research into counterconditioning by Mary Cover Jones and other investigators. Systematic desensitization involves training patients in procedures of muscular relaxation by which anxiety states may be inhibited. The patient then employs these procedures to countercondition a hierarchical series of imagined anxiety-provoking situations.

Carl Rogers postulates an innate tendency to actualize one's potentialities. He believes that people are innately good and that when they receive unconditional positive regard from others they will be better able to evaluate and change their own behaviors. In client-centered therapy, the goals of the therapist are not imposed on the client; the client talks about his most deeply felt emotions, with the therapist expressing understanding of the client's feelings but being careful not to condemn them.

Psychodrama is an expressive psychotherapeutic method developed in the 1930s by J. L. Moreno. It is an action-oriented procedure not limited to verbal exchange between patient and therapist, but employing group role-playing to help patients understand conflictive situations and feelings.

175-177. The answers are: 175-E, 176-D, 177-B. *(Suinn, pp 117, 275, 383-387.)* Sergei Korsakoff was a Russian psychiatrist who first described Korsakoff's psychosis in 1887. Patients with this psychosis appear to be clear instead of confused; however, on further examination they remember little beyond immediate observation or recent occurrences. They appear friendly and quite willing to answer questions about the past, but fabricate memories to conceal their amnesia. Poor nutrition, especially vitamin B deficiency from alcohol abuse, is the cause, although there is now some evidence that long-term alcohol use can cause brain damage with such symptoms even with good nutrition.

Eugene Bleuler proposed the diagnostic term "schizophrenia" in 1911, replacing "dementia praecox," which Emil Kraepelin had introduced 15 years previously. Kraepelin identified four disorders under this heading (simple, hebephrenic, catatonic, and paranoid). His subclassifications, together with the category of schizoaffective schizophrenia, continue in contemporary usage.

In the 1940s and 1950s, Rene Spitz achieved recognition for his psychoanalytically oriented research on the effects of early infantile separation from the mother. Working in orphanages, Spitz frequently observed a pattern of anaclitic depression of psychotic proportions. Separation commonly resulted in complete withdrawal, lack of social responsiveness, and general psychological deterioration; affected infants suffered high mortality despite provision of adequate physical care.

178-182. The answers are: 178-C, 179-E, 180-A, 181-B, 182-D. *(Hall, JF, pp 194-199.)* The variable ratio (VR) schedule of reinforcement is structured such that a variable and an unpredictable number of responses are required to produce a reinforcement. With time, a steady, smooth rate of response develops. This rate tends to be proportional to the average number of responses required for a reinforcement. VR schedules are sometimes termed "The Gambler's Schedule," reflecting a number of interesting parallels to the behavioral patterns associated with playing slot machines and roulette. It is characteristic of this behavior that it persists after reinforcement is discontinued.

Continuous reinforcement is regarded as the limiting case of all the other schedules. Normally, organisms on this schedule respond rapidly at first in order to accumulate a large number of reinforcements. Behavior then ceases as the reinforcements are consumed. Satiation from the concentrated reinforcement reduces the motivational levels such that responding may not resume for extended periods.

Intermittent responding is generally produced by fixed interval (FI) schedules. In such schedules, reinforcement is produced by the first response after a fixed time period following the previous reinforcement. To maximize the probability of reward, an organism must learn to time this period relatively accurately. The FI scallop appears in the response record when this timing behavior begins to occur. The scalloping effect results from a tendency to response-inhibition during the interval between the reinforcement and the next opportunity for reinforcement. Responding usually resumes slightly before the next reinforcement is available, and it is this sudden rise in response rate that produces the concave-upward scallop in the response tracing.

The fixed ratio (FR) schedule requires that a certain number of responses be emitted for each reinforcement. Normally, there is no restriction on the timing of this behavior. The response pattern generated by FR schedules is characterized by the "postreinforcement pause." This pattern results from an organism's tendency to cease responding, consume the reinforcer, and then wait for an additional refractory period before again responding.

The variable interval (VI) schedule does not show the scalloping that is characteristic of schedules having fixed temporal relationships among reinforcements. In the VI schedule, it is impossible to predict the time that must elapse between successive reinforcements. Organisms therefore tend to respond with a smooth, steady rate that is inversely proportional to the average time interval in the schedule.

183-187. The answers are: 183-D, 184-A, 185-E, 186-B, 187-C. *(Hall, CS, pp 279-288, 383-412, 487-508, 567-629.)* William Sheldon emphasizes the importance of constitutional differences in personality. In stressing the relationships between temperament and physique (somatotype), Sheldon identified three main somatotypes (endomorphy, mesomorphy, ectomorphy). He then attempted to connect these with three types of temperament (viscerotonia, somatotonia, cerebrotonia). Sheldon found endomorphy to be highly correlated with viscerotonia (individuals with a general love of comfort), mesomorphy to be highly correlated with somatotonia (individuals with a love of physical activity and adventure), and ectomorphy to be highly correlated with cerebrotonia (individuals who are withdrawn and inhibited).

Carl Rogers's theory of personality employs two main structural concepts—self and ideal-self. When the self and the ideal-self are incongruent, according to Rogers, the individual is maladjusted. Rogers argues that normally there is a basic tendency toward self-actualization, implying increasing alignment of self and the concept of ideal-self.

Neal Miller and John Dollard contributed an influential theory of social learning that stresses the importance of imitative behaviors in the acquisition of social skills and personality characteristics. Matched-dependent behavior refers to an imitative process that develops on the basis of positive reinforcement received for emulating the behavior of a model.

Hans Eysenck developed and experimentally tested a descriptive theory of personality based on the results of learning and conditioning principles. He also demonstrated the importance of genetic factors in personality development and played a major role in the origin and growth of behavior therapy. He argued that traditional methods of psychotherapy and psychoanalysis have no efficacy.

Kurt Lewin's field theory is an outgrowth of Gestalt psychology. He regarded behavior as a function of the psychological field forces that exist at the time the behavior occurs. Personality development occurs as the total field configuration becomes more and more differentiated within the life space, but with considerable permeability and interaction between the various units. Lewin relied heavily on such dynamic concepts as need, psychic energy, tension, force or vector, and valence.

188-192. The answers are: 188-B, 189-A, 190-A, 191-B, 192-C. *(Kandel, ed 2. pp 806-808.)* Classical conditioning involves the pairing (or association) of a conditional stimulus, such as a light or bell, with an unconditional stimulus, such as a shock or food. The conditional stimulus (light or bell) originally produces no response, while the unconditional stimulus (shock or food) produces a response called the unconditioned response (e.g., withdrawal or salivation). By repeatedly presenting the conditional stimulus just before the unconditional stimulus, the conditioned response can then be elicited by the conditional stimulus alone, as though the unconditional stimulus was being anticipated or predicted.

Operant conditioning (sometimes called instrumental conditioning or trial-and-error learning) is also associational learning in that it is the association between a response and a stimulus. Classical conditioning, on the other hand, is the formation of an association between two stimuli, the conditional and unconditional stimuli, and is generally restricted to specific reflex responses. Operant conditioning involves the reinforcing of behaviors that either occur spontaneously or with no recognizable eliciting stimuli. When such behaviors are either rewarded or result from the removal of noxious stimuli, they tend to reoccur and increase in the probability of occurrence. This process is known as reinforcement.

In classical conditioning, the conditioned response will decrease in intensity or probability of occurrence if the conditional stimulus is presented repeatedly without also presenting the unconditional stimulus. This is known as extinction or forgetting and also occurs in operant conditioning if the reinforcement does not occur. Behaviors followed by aversive or noxious consequences tend not to be repeated.

Historically, classical and operant conditioning have been regarded as dissimilar; however, classical and operant conditioning appear to be controlled by remarkably similar laws. The two kinds of learning appear to be manifestations of a common underlying neural mechanism.

Human Development

DIRECTIONS: Each question below contains five suggested responses. Select the **one best** response to each question.

193. Erik Erikson views the stage of young adulthood as being best described by a crisis of

(A) trust versus mistrust
(B) intimacy versus isolation
(C) identity versus role confusion
(D) initiative versus guilt
(E) autonomy versus dependence

194. All the following statements about aging are true EXCEPT

(A) the maximal life span has increased in populations over the past 20 years
(B) the risk of death increases exponentially with time
(C) life expectancy would increase only 20 years if heart disease and cancer were eliminated
(D) the biomedical model is becoming increasingly inapplicable in accounting for death in the elderly
(E) the $\dot{V}_{O_2\ max}$ can be used as an integrated measure of the functional limits of the whole body

195. According to current evidence on the status of an adolescent's identity, which of the following factors is the most stable during adolescence?

(A) Intimacy
(B) Achievement
(C) Diffusion
(D) Foreclosure
(E) Trust

196. According to current research, a daughter is most likely to have traditional personal vocational aspirations if she has a

(A) nonworking mother
(B) working mother
(C) mother in a traditionally masculine occupation
(D) working father
(E) high occupational status father

197. The term "learning disabilities" most often refers to problems in learning

(A) to do arithmetic
(B) to read
(C) to write compositions
(D) eye-hand coordination
(E) achievement orientation

198. Sequential studies of human development suggest that the growth of intelligence may continue through

(A) late adolescence
(B) early adulthood
(C) middle adulthood
(D) late adulthood
(E) old age

199. In studying human development, the remeasurement of a cross-sectional sample of people after a given fixed interval of time has passed is called

(A) time-lag design
(B) sequential design
(C) multivariate design
(D) cross-sectional design
(E) longitudinal design

200. All the following research findings on adult development are true EXCEPT that

(A) significant developmental changes continue to occur throughout adulthood
(B) as people age, there is an increasing range of differences between individuals
(C) changes in adulthood occur in all areas of development (cognitive, physical, and social-personal)
(D) adult cognitive changes may show quantitative reduction on an ability test, but a qualitative acquisition of a different form of intelligence
(E) just as is the case in childhood and adolescence, there are predominant and universal developmental stages in adulthood

201. In the theory developed by Jean Piaget, the first unit to appear in cognitive development is

(A) language
(B) schema
(C) concepts
(D) rules
(E) images

202. According to Freud, children pass through all the following psychosexual stages of development EXCEPT the

(A) oral
(B) anal
(C) phallic
(D) autoerotic
(E) genital

203. A prominent "embracing" response that can be elicited in a newborn infant by a sudden change in the head position is called the

(A) sign of Babinski
(B) startle (Moro's) reflex
(C) convulsive reflex
(D) infant carry response
(E) primate hug

204. Which of the following statements about the decline of sexual responsiveness in men and women is true?

(A) In men the decline is gradual and begins in their twenties, whereas female responsiveness does not start to decline until approximately age 60

(B) Responsiveness in both women and men begins to decline gradually in their twenties

(C) Responsiveness in men begins to decline in their forties, whereas in women it begins to decline in their thirties

(D) Responsiveness in men declines sharply in their fifties, whereas in women sexual responsiveness declines gradually beginning in their thirties

(E) In neither men nor women is there a significant decline in responsiveness until their sixties, when both decrease sharply

205. In comparing health behaviors of younger and older people, older people report all the following EXCEPT

(A) more symptoms
(B) less positive health status
(C) more vulnerability to health threats
(D) decline in regular physical activity
(E) improvement of eating habits

206. In the study of aging, the theory of disengagement refers to which of the following phenomena?

(A) A process whereby older persons tend to be neglected by their adult children

(B) A process whereby older persons become incapable of caring for themselves

(C) A withdrawal of emotional commitment by older persons to the outside world

(D) The psychological trauma caused by retirement

(E) The fact that marital satisfaction typically decreases with age

207. Erik Erikson's theory of the life cycle and growth of the ego is reflected in which of the following statements?

(A) Sexual drive is crucial in determining the development of a sense of identity

(B) Ego maturation is genetically predetermined; cultural influences are of minor importance

(C) There are eight stages characterized by crises whose satisfactory resolution is essential to the development of a healthy sense of identity

(D) There are five phases of development characterized in turn by aggressive, affiliative, achievement, nurturance, and power motives

(E) People are burdened with too many ego functions; society would benefit from stricter and more economic processes of socialization

208. Recent studies concerned with alcohol use and abuse in adolescence have found all the following to be true EXCEPT that

(A) alcohol is the most widely used drug by youth between the ages of 12 and 17
(B) adolescent problem drinkers use less illicit drugs than nondrinkers
(C) heavy drinking during adolescence is typically accompanied by other antisocial behaviors
(D) the most frequent cause of death and disability among youth today is traffic accidents, many of which are directly related to alcohol
(E) adolescent problem drinkers are more tolerant of deviance

209. All the following factors are found to be associated with atypical gender role behavior in boys EXCEPT

(A) rejection of a boy by his mother
(B) lack of a prototypical older male figure
(C) lack of male playmates during early childhood
(D) parental encouragement of "feminine" behaviors
(E) unusual physical attractiveness

210. All the following statements about prenatal and perinatal development are true EXCEPT that

(A) the developmental consequences of prematurity are resolved within the first 18 months
(B) prematurity is more frequent in mothers from lower socioeconomic groups
(C) maternal anxiety is associated with incidence of colic in the neonate
(D) marital conflict during pregnancy may affect the quality of early mother-child interaction
(E) the incidence of neonatal retardation is highest in mothers who are less than 20 or more than 35 years of age

211. In Rene Spitz's classic study of sensory deprivation, he found all the following to be true EXCEPT that

(A) social interaction with other humans is essential in infant development
(B) in the first 4 months, infants in the foundling home (having less contact with other people) scored better on several developmental indices than those in the nursing home
(C) by 1 year, the foundling home infants had fallen far below those in the nursing home
(D) after 2 or 3 years, most infants in the foundling home could not walk or talk
(E) children in the nursing home had a higher incidence of infection than those in the foundling home because of the many social contacts

212. Institutionalization during infancy often involves all the following consequences EXCEPT

(A) poor linguistic organization during early childhood
(B) deficits in concept formation and abstract thinking
(C) later impairment of motor skills
(D) anaclitic depression
(E) abnormal behavioral patterns

213. The complex of symptoms characteristic of children who are deprived of their mother or of a mother substitute during infancy and often extending into the first years of life is known as

(A) stranger anxiety
(B) anxiety neurosis
(C) autism
(D) childhood schizophrenia
(E) anaclitic depression

214. Which of the following statements about dependency behavior patterns in the preschool years is true?

(A) The degree of dependency on peers does not change significantly between 2 and 4 years of age
(B) Boys usually exhibit greater dependency than do girls
(C) Help-seeking behavior ("instrumental dependency") is constant from 3 to 5 years of age
(D) Intense dependency at age 5 or 6 portends dependency conflicts in adolescence and adulthood
(E) By age 5 or 6, dependency becomes an unstable personality trait with girls

215. Stages in the child's normal development of speech are characterized by all the following statements EXCEPT that

(A) between 1 and 6 months, infants invent new noises and experiment with them
(B) infants 4 to 5 months old will repeat sounds they hear
(C) infants between 12 and 18 months will intentionally use a word appropriate to the situation
(D) between 24 and 36 months, infants use 200 to 300 words in phrases and two-word sentences
(E) by 48 months of age, the child should have a vocabulary of about 1,500 words

216. Research findings on early gender-role identification and behaviors show that all the following statements are true EXCEPT that

(A) gender-related differences in play behavior are evident as early as 13 months
(B) males are generally more aggressive in their play and problem-solving activities than are females
(C) children who experience gender reassignment after the age of 2 are considered to be high-risk candidates for psychological disorders
(D) children between 3 and 4 years of age are able to make gender-appropriate choices according to Western stereotypes
(E) females 3 to 5 years old appear to be more concerned about gender-appropriate play activities than are males of a similar age

217. Which of the following statements about the development of moral standards during childhood is true?

(A) Only at puberty do a child's moral standards become independent of external rewards and punishments
(B) The development of guilt as a reaction to transgressions is fostered by parental warmth
(C) Children of 11 or 12 years of age are more likely to make inflexible, absolute moral judgments than those 7 or 8 years of age
(D) Older children are more likely than younger children to judge behavior as right or wrong in terms of its reinforcement outcomes
(E) The development of moral reasoning is independent of general intellectual maturation

DIRECTIONS: Each question below contains four suggested responses of which **one or more** is correct. Select

A	if	**1, 2, and 3**	are correct
B	if	**1 and 3**	are correct
C	if	**2 and 4**	are correct
D	if	**4**	is correct
E	if	**1, 2, 3, and 4**	are correct

218. Educational stimulation of disadvantaged children results in a subsequent improvement in cognitive and academic performance when stimulation

(1) occurs daily
(2) is maintained for an extensive period of time
(3) is instituted very early
(4) focuses on cognitive, language, and number skills

219. Compared with pregnant women aged 20 to 25, pregnant adolescents are more apt to have

(1) infants of lower birth weight
(2) inadequate prenatal care
(3) higher rates of infant mortality
(4) higher rates of birth defects and mental retardation

220. In comparing overweight adolescent boys and girls, girls are more apt to

(1) experience parental pressure to restrict food intake
(2) eat in response to negative and positive moods
(3) be blamed by their parents for their weight status
(4) interpret presence of other people as a signal for eating

221. In Piaget's theory of child development, the processes that allow a child to move from one stage of development to the next include which of the following?

(1) Reinforcement
(2) Equilibration
(3) Assimilation
(4) Accommodation

222. In attempting to understand how adolescents develop the habit of smoking, social learning theory is built on the observation of

(1) acquired expectations
(2) disinhibition
(3) learned behaviors
(4) fear stimulation

223. The phenomenon of parent-infant bonding proposed by Kenell and Klaus affects which of the following variables?

(1) Infant's language development
(2) Infant's cognitive development
(3) Amount of crying done by infant
(4) Length of breast feeding

224. Major obstacles for children in the creative solving of problems include

(1) failure to understand or grasp a problem
(2) forgetting certain aspects of a problem
(3) fear of failure
(4) insufficient knowledge

225. Children develop identification with a parent as a result of

(1) perception of similarities, physical and behavioral
(2) imitation of parental mannerisms
(3) communication from others concerning similarities
(4) attractiveness of the parent

226. Intelligence and cognitive development during adolescence are usually characterized by

(1) the emergence of hypothetico-deductive reasoning
(2) attitudes and reasoning that tend to be egocentric
(3) a growing capacity for probabilistic thinking
(4) a type of reasoning that subordinates reality to possibility

227. Prominent symptoms associated with the psychiatric diagnosis of "adjustment disorder" include

(1) substance abuse
(2) anxiety
(3) insomnia
(4) depression

228. Social factors that play a major role in influencing junior and senior high school students to smoke include

(1) peer pressure
(2) cigarette advertising
(3) modeling
(4) inoculation

229. When achievement motivation is emphasized and rewarded in early childhood, it is apt to produce

(1) feelings of personal worth
(2) tolerance for frustration
(3) higher levels of persistence
(4) lower goals than could be achieved

230. Cognitive skills of early childhood show which of the following patterns?

(1) At 18 months, a child begins to
follow simple one-part directions,
begins many questions with
"what," imitates people in his or
her environment, and infers causes
from observing effects
(2) At 2 years, the child begins to
learn about time sequences,
matches simple shapes and sizes,
attempts new solutions to old
problems, and may arrange several
words in grammatically incorrect
sentences
(3) At 3 years, the child asks many
"why" questions, talks in sentences using four or more words,
can give his first and last name,
and may talk about his fears
(4) At 4 years, the child may begin
many questions with "how,"
knows the days of the week, can
identify coins correctly, and can
follow a three-step direction in
proper order

231. Language development in childhood is characterized by which of the
following?

(1) Infants 15 to 20 weeks of age use
different patterns of vocalization to
identify discomforts such as hunger, fright, and pain
(2) Most children master all consonant
sounds by the age of 3 to 3½
years
(3) The first words spoken are usually
nouns
(4) Vowels emerge in hierarchical order between ages 3 and 7 years

232. Biological changes in the adolescent years include

(1) a growth spurt for girls with peak
velocity at 14 years of age
(2) menarche at any time between 10
and 16½ years of age; the average
now is just under 13 years of age
(3) a growth spurt for boys with peak
velocity at 12 years of age
(4) growth of testes beginning as early
as age 9½ or as late as age 13½
and ending at any time between
ages 13½ and 17 years

233. Childhood dreams

(1) start when the child is able to talk
(2) are experienced as pleasant more
often as the preschooler grows
older
(3) increase in frequency as the child
approaches the age of 5
(4) in the form of frightening nightmares occur at a relatively young
age (3 to 4)

SUMMARY OF DIRECTIONS

A	B	C	D	E
1, 2, 3 only	1, 3 only	2, 4 only	4 only	All are correct

234. Concepts of death at various stages of child development include that

(1) between birth and 2 years of age, separation is more apt to be experienced as synonymous with death
(2) children 3 and 4 years of age believe that a toy feels pain when it is broken
(3) children 5 to 6 years old fantasize that the dead person continues to experience emotion and biological function in the grave
(4) children 7 to 9 years of age realize the inevitability of death for all living things, no longer feel responsible for the death of others, and yet feel that death can be avoided

235. True statements concerning aging include which of the following?

(1) Twenty percent of aged persons live in long-stay institutions (nursing homes, mental hospitals, homes for the aged)
(2) The majority of old people feel miserable most of the time
(3) Aged drivers have more accidents per person than drivers under age 65
(4) All five senses tend to decline in old age

236. Alcohol consumption in pregnant females is associated with which of the following fetal risk factors?

(1) Decreased birth weight
(2) Mental retardation
(3) Increased spontaneous abortion
(4) Fetal alcohol syndrome

237. Chronic alcohol consumption by a pregnant woman can produce fetal alcohol syndrome with which of the following symptoms?

(1) Retardation of intrauterine growth
(2) Microcephaly
(3) Premature birth
(4) Reduction in number of fingers and toes

238. The incidence of smoking addiction among high school seniors

(1) is more influenced by caring adults than by peer pressure
(2) occurs in an upward trend from elementary and junior high school
(3) can be reduced significantly through fear arousal
(4) approaches the level of the general adult population

DIRECTIONS: Each group of questions below consists of lettered headings followed by a set of numbered items. For each numbered item select the **one** lettered heading with which it is **most** closely associated. Each lettered heading may be used **once, more than once, or not at all.**

Questions 239-242

For each description of a child's behavior below, select the age with which it is most closely associated as part of the growth and development sequence.

(A) 18 months
(B) 2 years
(C) 3 years
(D) 4 years
(E) 5 years

239. Cuts around pictures with scissors; buttons a small button; can copy a square

240. Can drink from a cup without much spilling; turns several pages of a book together; builds a tower of four or five blocks

241. Can copy a circle; can wash and dry hands; can brush teeth—but not adequately; begins to use blunt scissors

242. Can turn doorknobs that can be reached; can drink from small cup using one hand; builds a tower of six or seven blocks

Questions 243-246

Match each view of illness with the developmental age at which it is characteristic.

(A) Preschool age
(B) Elementary school age
(C) High school age
(D) Adult
(E) Elderly

243. Person views self as immortal or immune to external agents (e.g., germs)

244. Person views illness as putting friendships at risk

245. Person regards illness as a consequence of "bad" behavior

246. Person fears loss of control

Human Development
Answers

193. The answer is B. *(Lerner, 1980. pp 334-343.)* Erik Erikson's stage theory of psychosocial development provides descriptions of personality development that are consistent with a life-span perspective. It has served as a major basis for research on human development. Erikson views the individual as having to develop the capacities (the ego functions) to meet the expectations of society. At each of the eight stages of psychosocial development there is an accompanying "ego crisis." These stages are trust versus mistrust (birth to 1½ years), autonomy versus shame or doubt (1½ to 3 years), initiative versus guilt (3 to 6 years), industry versus inferiority (6 years to puberty), identity versus role confusion (adolescence), intimacy versus isolation (young adulthood), generativity versus stagnation (adulthood), and integrity versus despair (maturity). During intimacy versus isolation in the stage of young adulthood, there is psychosocial pressure for a person to form a close, stable interpersonal relationship. Thus, to the extent that one can attain an unconditional interchange and relationship, one will feel a sense of intimacy in feelings, ideas, and goals. If one cannot share and be shared, then one will feel a sense of isolation.

194. The answer is A. *(Andres, pp 82-101.)* In spite of advances in medical science, there has been no extension of the limit of the life span, although a greater proportion of the population is reaching the apparent biological limit of 85 plus or minus 10 years. It is estimated that life expectancy would increase only about 20 years if all heart disease and cancer were eliminated. In effect, prevention and intervention have improved cohort survival as specific causes of fatal diseases have been conquered. In general, the risk of death in the elderly increases exponentially with time. However, the biomedical model for diseases is not as applicable today since death increasingly occurs in the absence of disease. One series of studies has shown that some cells are apparently programmed for a fixed and limited number of reproductions, and then they die. This has provided some new concepts on aging and death. The $\dot{V}_{O_2 \text{ max}}$ has been determined to be an integrated measure of the functional limits of the whole body. Furthermore, the relative impairment and functional age of a person can be evaluated by the use of a simple monogram.

195. The answer is B. *(Lerner, 1980. pp 343-344.)* Among the identity statuses listed in the question, identity achievement is the most stable during adolescence. Most people move adaptively from other statuses toward identity achievement and hence resolve the crisis by virtue of occupational and ideological role commitment.

Those who have achieved identity usually show a commitment to an occupation or to an ideology, whereas those who are in a state of identity diffusion or confusion lack such commitment and often are not concerned about their lack of commitment. Adolescents in the status of foreclosure have generally not experienced a crisis, but have adopted the identities of their parents with little or no questioning of those identities. Intimacy also exists during adolescence, but is relatively unstable. Basic trust occurs much earlier (birth to 1½ years) and does play a role in adolescence as well as throughout life, but it is not a major factor in the adolescent's identity crisis.

196. The answer is A. *(Lerner, 1980. pp 388-391.)* When females develop within a family in which their mother is employed, they have less stereotyped views of female roles than do daughters of nonworking mothers, have a broader definition of female roles, and are more likely to emulate their mothers. It is hypothesized that homes with working mothers have different family interactions than do homes with nonworking mothers. The modeling influence for working and the development of achievement orientations appear to be major factors in developing nontraditional vocational aspirations. Also, fathers of high occupational status are more apt to promote nontraditional vocational achievement in their daughters. Interaction in such family settings may promote the development of vocational role orientations and behaviors that are nontraditional. In contrast, the daughter of a nonworking mother will be more influenced by the traditional model of the nonworking mother and will develop achievement orientations more consistent with the traditional female roles.

197. The answer is B. *(Lerner, 1980. pp 417-421.)* Learning disability is the label given to children who show a discrepancy between their estimated academic potential and their actual level of academic performance. Failure to learn academically does not necessarily imply general impairment in intellectual capacity, but it can seriously affect broad adaptive functioning. Most individuals with learning disabilities show a largely selective deficit, despite apparently normal schooling exposure, seemingly normative family settings, appropriate motivational predispositions, intact sense organs, adequate physical status, and normal intelligence, yet they fail to learn with normal proficiency. Research studies show that the criterion of failure to learn to read is the most frequent manifestation of a learning disability. This form of learning disability is generally known as dyslexia and is a problem of major proportions, especially during adolescence.

198. The answer is E. *(Lerner, 1980. pp 229-232.)* Studies of intelligence suggest that a person's IQ score is somewhat variable in the early years, becomes increasingly stable from birth through middle adolescence, and at about age 18 reaches a maximum score that is maintained for some time. Early cross-sectional studies indicated a decrease in IQ scores from middle adolescence into adulthood, but data from later longitudinal research indicated more stability or actual increases in scores.

In 1956, Schaie began to study 500 people ranging in age from 21 to 70. When the data were analyzed cross-sectionally, the adolescent to adulthood decline typically seen in such studies was observed, but when the data were looked at longitudinally within each of the birth cohort groups in their sequential design, a decline on only one of the four measures (visual-motor flexibility) of intelligence was found. Knowledge attained through education and socialization (e.g., verbal comprehension, number skills) and the ability to organize and process visual information resulted in a systematic increase in scores for all age groups. Clearly, the course of intellectual change from adolescence onward is not just an age-related phenomenon. One may expect that many of the levels and types of ability present in adolescence will be maintained or enhanced in the adult and aged years, in large part depending on such factors as education, experiences, and cognitive activities.

199. The answer is B. *(Lerner, 1980. pp 171-179.)* The four research designs for studying human growth and development are longitudinal design, cross-sectional design, time-lag design, and sequential design. In the longitudinal design, the same group of people are observed at more than one time. The cross-sectional design studies age groups at one time. The time-lag design allows a researcher to see differences in behavior associated with particular ages at various times in history. Instead of focusing on one cohort or one time of measurement, a time-lag design considers only one age level at different times of measurement, say 1950, 1960, 1970, and 1980. The sequential design combines features of longitudinal and cross-sectional designs so that the researcher may assess differences between groups owing to age, cohort, or time of testing. The sequential design involves the remeasurement of a cross-sectional sample of people after a given fixed interval of time, obtaining repeated measures from each of the different cohort groups included in a given cross-sectional sample, and obtaining data from retest control groups to assess the effects of retesting.

200. The answer is E. *(Brophy, pp 324-326.)* Although significant developmental changes continue to occur throughout adulthood, there is an increasing range of differences, or variability, between individuals of the same chronological age. Hence, there are no predominant and universal developmental stages in adulthood as one finds in childhood and adolescence. Even if such predominant stages could be defined, the age at which people experience such stages or the sequence in which they occur is much more variable. In adulthood, changes occur in all areas of development (cognitive, physical, and social-personal). These changes may be a quantitative change in level, rate, or degree or a qualitative change in the nature or type. Thus, an aging adult's level of performance on an ability test may be reduced quantitatively, but qualitatively different forms of intelligence unique to adulthood, such as wisdom, may be acquired. Positive growth and change are expected and encouraged in childhood and adolescence, but in adulthood society does not provide such expectations and encouragement. The full potential for adult development has not begun to be realized.

201. The answer is B. *(Lerner, 1983. pp 179-185.)* A schema is an abstract or mental representation of the original elements of an event and their relation to each other. Piaget viewed children as continually trying to make sense of their world by dealing actively with objects and people. An infant's schema for another person's face, for example, is most likely to emphasize a circular outline containing other circular elements that represent the eyes. As soon as a schema for an event is established, the child tends to show prolonged attention to those events and to show even more attention to those events that are a little different, but not extremely different, from the one that created the original schema. A new idea or object is thereby incorporated into an idea or schema the child has already developed.

202. The answer is D. *(Lerner, 1983. pp 64-69.)* Sigmund Freud believed that children pass through psychosexual stages that are characterized by the erogenous zone that gives the greatest pleasure during a specific stage. For example, during the oral stage in the first year of life, oral activities of feeding and biting supposedly supply the greatest pleasures. Gratification occurs by bowel movements in the anal stage during the second and third years. During the fourth and fifth years, termed the phallic stage, the genital area becomes a primary source of pleasure. The genital stage occurs in adolescence, when the genitals mature and love objects are formed. It is asserted that if the emotional experiences associated with a given zone or stage are too intensely pleasurable, children may develop a fixation at the corresponding stage of development. In such cases, emotional development is retarded. Autoerotic is not a Freudian stage, but merely refers to the self-stimulation of sexual sensations.

203. The answer is B. *(Lerner, 1983. pp 150-154.)* Moro's reflex, known as the startle reflex, is an innate response to unexpected changes in head position, or sometimes to any surprising event. The reflex involves extension of the arms laterally, extension of the fingers, and then return of the hands to midline as if grasping someone. Developmentally, this reflex begins to disappear at 3 to 4 months and is usually gone by 6 months of age. It is believed that the disappearance of Moro's reflex coincides with functional maturation of the neocortex. Presumably, the cortex inhibits brain stem centers that mediate such early reflex responses.

204. The answer is A. *(Botwinick, ed 3. pp 94-102.)* Alfred Kinsey found that male sexual responsiveness, as measured by total sexual outlet, reaches a peak in the late teens and declines gradually thereafter, with no age period showing a greater decrease than any other. He found no significant decreases in female responsiveness, however, until age 60. Even so, female responsiveness after age 60 does not decline to the extent that male responsiveness does. However, Kinsey's sample indicated that males were more sexually active at all ages than were females.

205. The answer is B. *(Rosen, pp 205-214.)* In general, there is a gradual improvement of health behaviors with age. In children aged 8 to 15 there is a decline in health behaviors with decreasing regularity in eating and sleeping, and an increase in new risk behaviors such as smoking and drinking. In young adulthood, this pattern reverses itself with gradual improvements in health behavior, including eating habits. The health behavior that does not improve with age is physical exertion. This is unfortunate since lack of exercise shows the highest level of association with illness and mortality in the aged. In spite of older individuals reporting more symptoms, they also report themselves as being in more positive health status, especially people over the age of 60.

206. The answer is C. *(Atchley, ed 4. pp 242-243.)* The theory of disengagement, formulated by E. Cumming and W. E. Henry, refers to the withdrawal of emotional commitment from the environment that occurs in some older individuals. According to this theory, as people get older their world shrinks; they become less involved in the demands of society and more concerned with their immediate needs. This withdrawal is reciprocated by a lessening of interest in the older person by society.

207. The answer is C. *(Lerner, 1983. pp 69-70, 205-209.)* Erik Erikson's theory of ego development defines eight "crises" during the life cycle. Each crisis is critical to the development of a sense of personal identity. Although these crises are partly related to the five stages of psychosexual development delineated by classic psychoanalysis, Erikson tends to give greater emphasis to the growth of ego functions as independent of libidinal drive and more related to psychosocial than psychosexual development. As such, they are related to adaptive demands placed on the individual by society and involve a life-span perspective. The eight crises are basic trust versus basic mistrust, autonomy versus shame and doubt, initiative versus guilty functioning, industry versus inferiority, identity versus role confusion, intimacy versus isolation, generativity versus stagnation, and integrity versus despair.

208. The answer is B. *(Rosen, pp 42-45.)* Alcohol is clearly the most widely used drug by youth between the ages of 12 and 17, and the problem drinkers use much more illicit drugs than nondrinkers and typically exhibit other antisocial behaviors. These behaviors appear to make them more tolerant of deviance, especially since problem drinkers are less religious, less successful in school, and more concerned with independence than with academic pursuit. Traffic accidents, many related to alcohol use, are the most frequent cause of death and disability of youth.

209. The answer is A. *(Kaplan, ed 4. pp 4, 433-434.)* Atypical gender role development in boys is associated with a lack of male playmates during early childhood, lack of an older male to serve as a role model, unusual physical attractiveness, parental encouragement of "feminine" behavior, and maternal overprotection. Paternal rejection, but not maternal rejection, has also been found to be associated with such development. Young boys, especially between the ages of 2 and 4, often show an interest in so-called feminine activities and pastimes; however, what seems to differentiate boys whose gender development is atypical from those who develop normally is that the parents of the former do not discourage—indeed, may actively encourage—such behavior. Boys with atypical gender development may be prone to homosexual orientation in later life.

210. The answer is A. *(Lerner, 1983. pp 119-140.)* Developmental differences between premature and full-term children may still be evident at 4 to 6 years of age. The effects of prematurity include decrements of height and weight, as well as slower acquisition of motor and cognitive skills. Prematurity is more frequent among women from lower socioeconomic groups than among women in more fortunate circumstances, and premature babies born to such mothers recover less quickly from developmental deficits than do children from higher socioeconomic families.

211. The answer is E. *(Kandel, ed 2. p 758.)* In the 1940s, Rene Spitz compared the development of infants in a foundling home (much less contact with other human beings) with those in a prison's nursing home (where the mothers were allowed to spend time with their children). Both facilities provided good medical care and nutrition. After 4 months the foundling home infants actually scored better on several developmental indices (perhaps a genetic influence), but by 12 months the foundling home children had fallen far below the nursing home children. Further, many of the foundling home children had developed an anaclitic depression, were withdrawn with little curiosity or happiness, and were prone to infection. The nursing home children were similar to children raised in normal families after 2 or 3 years— walking well and talking actively. Of the 26 foundling home children, only 2 were able to walk or speak, and they could only say a few words. Spitz's findings have been confirmed by subsequent investigators, demonstrating that social interaction with other humans is essential in development, and that severe social and sensory deprivation in early childhood can have catastrophic consequences for later development.

212. The answer is C. *(Simons, ed 3. pp 140-147.)* Many psychological and behavioral deficiencies are associated with institutionalization and inadequate primary caretaking during infancy. There is frequently an initial motor retardation, but permanent impairment of motor skills is not usually observed. However, absence of primary caretakers and inadequate institutional arrangements have been implicated in deficiencies of emotional responsiveness and general intellectual functioning, particularly conceptual reasoning, as well as abnormal behavioral and emotional patterns. The irreversibility of such impairments caused by early deprivation is a matter of some controversy.

213. The answer is E. *(Kaplan, ed 4. pp 771-778.)* Anaclitic depression refers to the complex of symptoms exhibited by young children who are deprived of their mother or of a mother surrogate during the first few years of life. This reaction is made up of a number of stages. On first being separated from its caretaker, an infant will protest vigorously. If the caretaking figure is not restored to the infant, the infant enters what is known as the phase of despair and ceases protesting. This phase can be followed by a refusal to eat, which sometimes is fatal, or by a phase of detachment in which the infant withdraws from any interaction and engages in various forms of self-stimulation.

214. The answer is D. *(Mussen, ed 6. pp 13-14.)* By 5 or 6 years of age, dependency is a moderately stable personality trait. Recent studies validate its predictive validity—thus, an overly dependent 5-year-old is liable to have dependency conflicts during adolescence and adulthood. However, the predictive value of this trait is much stronger for girls than for boys. In this respect, dependent behavior at 5 years of age manifests the obverse pattern to aggressive behavior: aggression is a more stable personality trait for boys than for girls, whereas dependency is more stable for girls.

215. The answer is B. *(Schuster, ed 2. p 272.)* In order to assess the normal development of a child, it is important to understand the complex process and sequence of developmental skills that are involved in acquiring speech. Starting in the first 6 months of life, babies invent new noises and appear to experiment with them. Cooing usually begins around 2 months of age and occurs especially when the babies appear to be happy. By 4 or 5 months, babbling occurs. This is the practice of expressing alternative vowel and consonant sounds such as "baba." Babbling is an important skill to acquire before a child can learn to repeat sounds heard from other humans. Between 6 and 9 months of age, babies begin to repeat sounds or sound combinations that they have heard and advance to the lalling stage. Within the next several months, the babies attempt to imitate all and any sounds they hear. They begin to select those sounds that help them communicate their wants or that amuse them. Between 24 and 36 months of age, infants will be able to use 200 to 300 words in phrases and two-word sentences. By the age of 48 months, a child should have a vocabulary of about 1,500 words that can be used in short sentences with almost 100 percent intelligibility.

216. The answer is E. *(Schuster, ed 2. p 321.)* Significant gender-role identification and behaviors are learned early in life. Gender-related differences in play behaviors are evident as early as 13 months of age. Males are generally more aggressive in their play and problem-solving activities than are females. These early behaviors are apparently so critical to one's core gender identity that children who experience gender reassignment after the age of 2 are high-risk candidates for psychological disorders. Recent research involving choices in child play indicates that children 3 to 4 years of age are able to make gender-appropriate choices according to Western stereotypes. Three- to five-year-old male children appear to be more concerned about gender-appropriate play activities than are females at that age. This continues into adolescence, as adolescent males also appear to be more conscious of gender roles than are females of that age.

217. The answer is B. *(Mussen, ed 6. pp 363-365.)* While the cognitive development the child undergoes brings about a great awareness of moral values and standards, orientation to abiding by them depends on other factors, primarily identification with the parents and the experiencing of guilt for violation of guidelines. The development of conscience can be seen in internal reactions to transgressions in the form of guilt or by the child's taking up of standards that the child feels personally responsible for maintaining. A number of studies indicate that conscience development is fostered by the presence of parental love and warmth of a degree adequate for positive identification and modeling. Such positive identification and modeling more readily occur if the parent's own conscience and moral standards are mature and reasonable rather than either deficient or overly strict, harsh, and inflexible.

218. The answer is E (all). *(Mussen, ed 6. pp 291-295.)* Over the past 2 decades, many programs have attempted to improve the school performance of children from lower-class or disadvantaged homes. Most such studies have focused on developing competencies and motivational patterns that would provide the skills necessary to improve cognitive and academic performance. In general, they have demonstrated considerable success in improving subsequent cognitive and academic performance, including IQ. The degree of success is most often related to instituting the educational stimulation as early as possible; focusing directly on cognitive, language, and number skills; maintaining the effort over a prolonged period of time (years); and providing the stimulation on a daily basis rather than occasional exposure. These studies have also shown the importance of recognizing the powerful forces exerted on children by the values of the family and the community and the patterns of identification with social class and ethnic groups, so that a few isolated months or years of intervention cannot always offset the conditions and influences of the socioeconomically disadvantaged child. Programs that have been declared as unsuccessful in enhancing the intellectual functioning and academic success of such disadvantaged children have most often failed to provide one or more of the four listed components.

219. The answer is E (all). *(Lerner, 1980. pp 446-453.)* Children born to adolescents are more likely to be of low birth weight than children born to older women. These children also have higher rates of infant mortality, mental retardation, and birth defects. All the tendencies apply across different races. Pregnant adolescents are also less likely to have had adequate prenatal care, the maternal death rate for adolescents is higher, and they are more apt to suffer from medical complications such as toxemia and anemia and from poor nutrition.

220. The answer is A (1, 2, 3). *(Rosen, pp 96-98.)* Puberty is associated with important biological and psychological changes, especially in females with proliferation of fat cells, and general shifts in body image in reference groups from family to peers and in perceived identity. Parents attempt to exert considerable pressure to restrict their food intake, more so for girls than boys. Parents are unlikely to blame their sons for a weight problem, but regard their daughters' obesity in terms of problematic eating behavior and actively attempt to restrain their eating behaviors. Attempting to apply strict parental restrictions on eating tends to minimize options for learning self-control skills. Daughters are generally more apt to eat in response to both negative and positive mood. Exposure to more restraint may lead weight-conscious females to regard the presence of other people as a signal for not eating or for eating smaller portions.

221. The answer is C (2, 4). *(Lerner, 1983. pp 179-182.)* Assimilation is the addition of a new concept or object into a cognitive scheme already possessed by a child. Generally, this process involves the application of known rules to new objects and situations. Accommodation is the process of adapting one's rules or schemes to include new information, objects, or ideas. Each successive accommodation is a step toward cognitive maturity. Equilibration is the process of changing one's ideas about the world through accommodation to make them consistent with reality.

222. The answer is A (1, 2, 3). *(Rosen, p 24.)* Social learning theory, developed by Bandura, suggests that through observation children acquire certain expectations and learned behavior with regard to smoking. They can learn vicariously, for example, that smoking appears to relieve tension or anxiety. Also, when they observe a model appearing to enjoy the behavior, and without negative consequences, a condition of disinhibition results. The young person's learned expectation of negative consequences does not occur, and the expectation of negative consequences becomes weakened. This becomes an important factor in the ultimate decision regarding smoking.

223. The answer is E (all). *(Klaus, ed 2. pp 35-48.)* While background variables of economic status, race, culture, housing, education, parity, and age are more important variables in determining subsequent behavior of infants, the phenomenon of parent-infant bonding has recently been shown to be important also. The bonding that occurs during the critically sensitive period from the first hours and weeks of life has been shown to affect such factors as language development, cognitive development, length of breast feeding (which may be both a cause and an effect), amount of crying done by infant, touching and fondling by parent, failure to thrive, and subsequent child abuse or neglect. There are extensive animal studies that demonstrate the importance of biological bonding.

224. The answer is E (all). *(Mussen, ed 6. pp 219-221.)* Common barriers to the creative solution of problems by young children include failure to understand or grasp a problem or forgetting certain aspects of it, fear of failure, and insufficient knowledge. Such barriers may produce solutions that are novel but not creative; that is, their solutions may be unique but impractical or inefficient. Experience seems to be important in facilitating problem solving.

225. The answer is E (all). *(Mussen, ed 6. pp 391-394.)* Children identify with their parents because they want to and, involuntarily, because of a perception of similarities. Insofar as most parents are seen by a child as having desirable attributes (e.g., power, freedom, ready access to pleasures, mastery over the environment), the child, wishing to become the same, identifies with his or her parents. If the parents should provide such poor models that the identification process is hampered, the child is then likely to identify with other significant adults in his or her environment.

226. The answer is E (all). *(Conger, ed 3. pp 158-167.)* Many of the cognitive and personality changes that characterize adolescence may be related to the emergence of formal operational thought during puberty. Formal reasoning enlists cognitive structures that enable adolescents to subject real occurrences to speculative yet systematic thinking about probable consequences. Such thinking, essential to hypothetico-deductive methods, underpins certain adolescent views relating to idealism, romanticism, and egocentrism.

227. The answer is C (2, 4). *(Kaplan, ed 4. pp 476-479.)* The most prominent symptoms associated with the psychiatric diagnosis of "adjustment disorder" are anxiety and depression. The American Psychiatric Association's *Diagnostic and Statistical Manual of Mental Disorders,* 3rd edition *(DSM-III),* defines an "adjustment disorder" as a maladaptive reaction to a clearly identifiable event or events or adverse circumstances. In general, it is a pathological or maladaptive response to the stress of an ordinary life event or circumstance, such as loss of parent, divorce, business difficulties, loss of job, intrafamily disorders, or retiring. The basis of the disorder can be viewed as the person's experiencing of trauma as psychic overload with the response being disproportionately intense. The ability of the person to participate in the ordinary activities of everyday life is impaired. The most common symptoms are anxiety, depression, irritability, and physical complaints. Assault, reckless driving, defaulting of legal responsibilities, excessive drinking, and withdrawal can also occur. A concurrent physical disorder or chronic disease may make a person more vulnerable to an adjustment disorder.

228. The answer is A (1, 2, 3). *(Rosen, pp 26-30.)* The modeling of parents, teachers, and "significant others" has been found to play a major role in influencing a person to smoke. Peer pressure is also a major influence, especially in adolescence

Cigarette advertising, which may use celebrity models and link smoking to such attractions as sports, sex, and prestige, impresses youth with the pleasurable, grown-up, and no-risk aspects of smoking. Inoculation is a process whereby individuals are inoculated with arguments and behavioral skills to reinforce the effects of positive modeling, the social skills to counteract peer pressure to smoke, and various content analyses of the techniques used by advertisers to persuade youth to smoke.

229. The answer is A (1, 2, 3). *(Brophy, p 131.)* Mastery motivation, achievement motivation, frustration tolerance, level of aspiration, and feelings of competence are traits that begin to develop in early childhood and are directly affected by the encouragement, reward, and expectations of parents and other adults. The old assertion holds true that success breeds success expectations and failure breeds failure expectations. These expectations are strongly affected by the expectations and reactions of others. If reaction to the pursuit of goals is positive, then children are more apt to feel satisfied and proud and to develop stronger feelings of personal worth. Greater tolerance for frustration is also developed when a child's efforts are encouraged effectively, resulting in stronger achievement motivation and persistence to set and accomplish higher, but realistic, goals. These goals may be beyond their present abilities, but they are eventually within reach. Children who are shamed, ridiculed, or discouraged are more likely to develop feelings of insecurity and inadequacy and fear of failure. Also, they are more apt to set either low goals that they can reach or unrealistically high goals that they may never reach or never try to reach.

230. The answer is A (1, 2, 3). *(Schuster, ed 2. p 230.)* Cognitive skills in children develop in a fairly predictable pattern. Most cognitive behaviors can be expected to emerge chronologically. In comparing average age with expected behaviors of early childhood, one can expect the average 18-month-old child to begin many questions with "what," imitate almost everything in his or her environment, understand space only from his or her own activity of moving through it, begin to follow simple one-part directions, and begin to infer causes from observing effects. The average 2-year-old can be expected to begin to learn about time sequences (e.g., "after lunch"), may arrange several words together in grammatically incorrect two- or three-word sentences, matches simple shapes and colors, attempts new solutions to old problems, and demonstrates a beginning cooperation in toilet training by anticipating a need to "go." By the age of 3, the child can be expected to ask many "why" questions, talks in sentences using four or more words, may talk about his fears, can give his first and last name, and may explore the environment outside the home if given the chance; in addition many retain urine through a night's sleep and wake up dry. By the age of 4 years, the child begins many questions with "where," may talk with an imaginary playmate, may threaten to "run away from home," can give opposites of up-down, and hot-cold, and so on, and can associate familiar holidays with their seasons. Asking questions with "how," knowing the days of the week, identifying coins correctly, and following a three-step direction in proper order usually does not occur until the age of 5 years. At 5 years, the child may also begin asking the meaning of words, talks more "constantly," and may need to be reminded to eat or go to the bathroom because attention is so externally focused that he may fail to recognize subtle internal physiological cues. Knowing the average age at which certain cognitive skills can be expected to develop can be of great assistance in helping the physician monitor the normal, or typical, growth or development of individual children.

231. The answer is B (1, 3). *(Schuster, ed 2. pp 264-265.)* Before a child begins to talk, he uses a variety of vocalizations to express himself and to communicate with others. The 15- to 20-month-old child frequently emits long vocalizations that are qualitatively differentiated to communicate discomforts such as hunger, pain, or fright. Vocalizations of very young infants generally consist of vowel sounds. Most children master all the vowel sounds of American English by the age of 3 to 3½ years. Consonants emerge in hierarchical order as mastered phonemes between ages 3 and 7. Some consonants are more difficult to produce than others and are mastered later in the development sequence. The first words spoken are usually nouns.

232. The answer is C (2, 4). *(Lerner, 1983. pp 320-331.)* Growth spurts occur for both boys and girls. A growth spurt for girls usually has its peak velocity at 12 years of age, whereas the growth spurt for boys will have a peak velocity at 14 years of age. Although the adolescent growth spurt for girls typically begins at age 10½ and ends at age 14, it can start as early as age 9½ and end as late as age 15. Similarly, menarche can come at any time between the ages of 10 and 16½ and tends to be a late event of puberty. The adolescent growth spurt of boys can begin as early as age 10½ or as late as 16 and can end anywhere from age 13½ to 17½. Growth of the testes can begin as early as age 9½ and as late as 13½ and end at any time between the ages of 13½ and 17.

233. The answer is E (all). *(Schuster, ed 2. pp 226-227.)* Piaget and his associates report that the youngest age at which definite proof of dreaming is observed ranges from 21 months to 2 years of age. The evidence indicates that dreams do not occur until the child is able to talk and thereby symbolically manipulate events. The frequency of dreams, as well as their content, tends to change in different phases of the development process. Dreaming appears to increase in frequency as children approach the age of 5. Nightmares occur at a relatively young age (3 to 4). Pleasant dreams occur more often as the preschooler grows older.

234. The answer is E (all). *(Schuster, ed 2. pp 407-413.)* Although a child's discovery of death is a private and individual experience, it is closely related to cognitive and affective developmental stages. Cognitively, a child must be able to conceptualize animate versus inanimate objects, comprehend cause-effect relationships, and deal with concrete factors before dealing with the abstract. Affectively, sufficient ego-strength, separateness, uniqueness, vulnerability, and coping skills must be developed. The infant must develop a concept of self before being able to comprehend "me—not me."

Between birth and 2 years of age, the infant is aware of separation through object loss and separation anxiety. This separation or loss or deprivation is an early form of experiencing perceived as something synonymous with death. Children 3 and 4 years of age believe that all things think, feel, and experience things as they do. Thus they think that a toy feels pain when it is broken and that it must feel hurt when it is repaired. Also, they consider death as another form of life. At 4 and 5 years of age they believe that death is a cessation of movement, but that the dead person or animal continues to experience feelings. Cross-cultural studies have identified many primitive peoples as conceptualizing death on this level, since many of them place food, drink, and other objects at the grave or in the tomb of the deceased. Our custom of placing flowers and other adornments on graves may, in part, be a remnant of this level of conceptualizing death. Children at this age are also apt to associate death with retaliation or punishment, which may lead them to fear, anger, and aggression toward others. Physicians must be aware of this possible interpretation of the 5- and 6-year-old child as a reaction to death, especially in the child's own family.

At 5 or 6 years of age children are apt to feel that death can be avoided and that they are not responsible for another person's death. They also begin to realize that their own significant others can die, and this can lead to notable uncertainties and insecurities. Children at 7 to 9 years of age begin to accept the inevitability of death for all living things, but believe that somehow it is external to oneself. By 10 to 12 years of age, death begins to be accepted as a biological finality and understood in relation to natural laws, rather than being perceived as the result of aggression or trauma. Adolescents and even adults sometimes find it difficult to accept the concept of nonexistence, even though they are capable of abstract thought.

235. The answer is D (4). *(Brophy, pp 339-340.)* A major problem in attempting to provide health care for the elderly is understanding and counteracting some of the common stereotypes of aging. Although it is generally true that all five senses tend to decline in old age, it is not true that most old people feel miserable most of the time. In fact, recent studies show that the majority of the aged see themselves as being as happy as they were when they were younger. Boredom and lack of meaningful activity do become major factors with some aged, however. Another misconception is that a high percentage of the aged population live in long-stay institutions, such as nursing homes, mental hospitals, and homes for the aged. Actually, only about 5 percent of persons 65 and over, and about 10 percent of persons age 75 and over, are in long-stay institutions. Attempting to retain one's social, physical, and cognitive independence is a dominating factor and priority among the aged. Also, contrary to the stereotype that older drivers have a high automobile accident rate, older drivers have about the same accident rate per person as middle-aged drivers and a lower rate than drivers under age 30.

236. The answer is E (all). *(Hamburg, pp 43-45.)* Fetal alcohol syndrome is a high risk factor for pregnant women who drink heavily during pregnancy. It is characterized by certain morphological abnormalities and is frequently associated with mental retardation. Even two drinks daily of alcohol during pregnancy can also result in significantly decreased birth weight, and consumption levels as low as two drinks twice a week can increase the spontaneous abortion rate. Other adverse effects implicating alcohol consumption during pregnancy are lowered viability at birth, heart rate abnormalities, poor sucking ability, and other behaviors associated with poor functioning of the central nervous system. Cigarette smoking combined with alcohol consumption during pregnancy results in an increased, and possibly potentiated, risk.

237. The answer is A (1, 2, 3). *(Mussen, ed 6. pp 64-65.)* Fetal alcohol syndrome can occur as the result of chronic heavy drinking by a pregnant woman. Symptoms may include severe retardation of intrauterine growth, premature birth, microcephaly, and other deformities such as congenital eye and ear problems, heart defects, extra fingers and toes, and patterns of disturbed sleep. Most recent research suggests a 10 percent risk of this syndrome if the pregnant woman drinks as little as 2 to 4 ounces of hard liquor daily. It is estimated that 6,000 infants a year suffer from the effects of fetal alcohol syndrome.

238. The answer is C (2, 4). *(Rosen, pp 22-30.)* Peer pressure has been found to be more influential than any adult involvement in pre-adult smoking behavior. Even well-intentioned adults are often labeled as adult "naggers." Smoking often begins in elementary school, but most significantly in junior high school, and continues in an upward trend into high school, where by the senior year smoking addiction approaches the level of that in the general adult population. Fear arousal has not been shown to be very effective in attempts to educate youth against smoking, alcohol use, or drug abuse.

239-242. The answers are: 239-D, 240-A, 241-C, 242-B. *(Schuster, ed 2. p 200.)* The development of both gross and fine motor skills has been clearly observed and scientifically documented for various ages and stages of development. At the age of 18 months, a child can run, climb, throw a small ball, drink from a cup without much spilling, turn several pages of a book together, unzip a large zipper, scribble with a pencil, and build a tower of four or five blocks.

At 2 years of age, a child can try to jump, can turn doorknobs that can be reached, can drink from a small cup using only one hand, turn pages of a book one at a time, unbutton large buttons, and build a tower of six or seven blocks.

At 3 years of age, a child can peddle a tricycle, jump from a low step, begin to use blunt scissors, copy a circle, wash hands and brush teeth (but not adequately), and imitate a bridge made of three blocks.

At age 4, a child can hop forward on one foot, walk backward, cut around pictures with scissors, copy a square, button side buttons, and may bathe self with assistance.

At 5 years of age, a child can jump rope, stand up without using hands, may be able to print own name, copy a triangle, dress without assistance, eat with a fork, and put toys away neatly.

243-246. The answers are: 243-C, 244-B, 245-A, 246-E. *(Schneiderman, pp 257-275, 547-548.)* An individual's developmental level directly affects cognitive social, emotional, and behavioral factors in illness. Chronological age is of less value to the health professional in assessing and anticipating problems in treatment and prevention. Individuals with mental or physical handicaps can be particularly difficult to assess and predict.

Preschool children generally see being sick as the result of some external agent (e.g., germs). They believe that getting well depends on strict adherence to rigid health rules. They are also more apt to view hospitalization as a punishment for bad behavior. This makes preparatory procedures especially important prior to and during hospitalization in order to deal with anxiety and stress. Because of close ties between the preschool child and parents, separation from parents can be an extreme source of stress for both the child and the family.

In early elementary school years, regular friendship patterns and peer contacts increase in importance. School absences from illness can put these friendships at risk. A physical, mental, or educational handicap can also provide special difficulties in making and maintaining new peer relationships.

In adolescence, the complexities of illness and health and the more sophisticated interaction of internal and external factors becomes more prominent. The long-range consequences of an illness are not apparent, however, and the adolescent views himself or herself as indestructable or immortal. Peer group activities are of extreme importance. Adolescents will deny or neglect their medical care or health so as not to appear "different." Diabetes provides special difficulties. Peer pressures to drink or smoke can also undermine present or future health.

A major concern of the elderly is the possibility of developing a debilitating illness. The fear is that they might lose control of their mental and physical abilities and become dependent on or rejected by significant others. Other concerns are possible disfigurement or handicap, impending death, extended pain, chronic hospitalization, and invalid status.

Communication and Interaction

DIRECTIONS: The questions below contain five suggested responses. Select the **one best** response to each question.

247. Which of the following statements best describes the Likert technique of attitude measurement?

(A) Subjects indicate on five-point scales the extent of their agreement with a set of attitude statements

(B) Subjects indicate whether they agree with each of a series of attitude statements, which are equally spaced along an attitude continuum

(C) Subjects' responses to an open-ended interview are coded by content analysis

(D) Subjects judge a particular concept on a series of bipolar semantic scales

(E) Subjects check all acceptable items in a set of statements arranged in order of ''difficulty of acceptance''

248. A major characteristic of the usual physician-patient relationship is

(A) reluctance to recognize the physician's authority

(B) repression of childlike desire to give up responsibility

(C) active participation in treatment

(D) position of equal power vis-à-vis the physician

(E) situational dependency on the physician

249. Interpersonal relationship studies have concluded that the most critical element to assure compliance behavior in a physician-patient relationship is

(A) the exchange of accurate information and facts

(B) the congruence of expectations of physician and patient

(C) similarity of physician's and patient's age

(D) recognition and down-playing of social class differences between physician and patient

(E) allowing for the patient to be rewarded in some way for compliance

250. All the following are important
in informing a patient or a patient's
relative of the patient's serious illness
EXCEPT

(A) establishing clearly that you would
   prefer to talk about it only after
   you have all the facts, tests, and
   other relevant information
(B) finding out what the individual
   thinks or knows about the illness
(C) finding out what the individual
   wants to know about the illness
(D) giving honest answers in such a
   way as to leave the individual with
   some realistic hope
(E) determining the individual's understanding of what you have discussed

DIRECTIONS: Each question below contains four suggested responses of which **one or more** is correct. Select

A	if	**1, 2, and 3**	are correct
B	if	**1 and 3**	are correct
C	if	**2 and 4**	are correct
D	if	**4**	is correct
E	if	**1, 2, 3, and 4**	are correct

251. David McClelland's research on power developed which of the following concepts?

(1) Oppressive power
(2) Personal power
(3) Productive power
(4) Socialized power

252. The recent Stanford University community health education study attempting to modify health benefits, health motivation, and personal health habits showed which of the following results?

(1) Cigarette smoking, egg consumption, and cholesterol levels declined in both test communities
(2) The control community made important achievements
(3) The mass media campaign plus the behavioral modification training achieved the most significant results
(4) It is better to focus on one public medium of communication at a time

253. In opening an initial interview with a patient, it is important to

(1) state what you already know concerning the problem
(2) refrain from duplicating questions already gathered in the chart
(3) ask the patient why he or she has come
(4) project an image of knowledge and authority

254. Which of the following can be considered to be nonverbal communication?

(1) Touch
(2) Gesture and posture
(3) Dress and grooming
(4) Physical distance

255. In judging facial expressions, which of the following emotions can be easily recognized and differentiated in most cultures?

(1) Happiness
(2) Fear
(3) Sadness
(4) Surprise

SUMMARY OF DIRECTIONS

A	B	C	D	E
1, 2, 3 only	1, 3 only	2, 4 only	4 only	All are correct

256. Studies on communications between physicians and patients have demonstrated that

(1) the less information furnished by the doctor, the less the compliance
(2) providing little or no information to patients results in a higher level of patient dissatisfaction than any other aspect of medical care
(3) lower-class individuals tend to receive less information than do upper-class individuals
(4) physicians most often are too explicit in communicating their intentions and would generate less frustration if they were less explicit

257. In the interaction between physicians and patients, the physician is often unaware of the

(1) emotional impact of "matter-of-fact" statements the physician may make
(2) communication obstacles of technical jargon
(3) effects of data overload on the patient
(4) patient's need for the physician to maintain the power relationship

258. Statements about patients' or physicians' perceptions of symptoms that are generally true include which of the following?

(1) Physicians tend to focus on symptoms that have serious implications for future health
(2) Patients tend to focus on the degree of discomfort rather than the amount or degree of tissue damage
(3) Patients often focus on symptoms that interfere with usual activities or routines
(4) Physicians usually focus on symptoms according to visibility or recognizability

259. Physicians tend to inspire trust on the basis of their

(1) self-confidence
(2) willingness to listen
(3) willingness to socialize
(4) ability to make a quick diagnosis

260. In a study of patients' views of the physician-patient relationship, it has been found that hospitalized patients

(1) perceive few areas in which they can exercise any control
(2) find it difficult to assess the competence of physicians and other health professionals
(3) cannot define the care and services they should expect or demand
(4) are not concerned with cooperating with their physicians

261. Patients evaluate the competence of their physicians according to which of the following guidelines?

(1) The degree to which a physician's behavior fits the expectations of society at large
(2) The degree to which a physician's behavior fits the expectations of a patient's subculture
(3) What a patient learns from the experiences of others
(4) A patient's own experience with a physician

262. Studies of verbal interactions between physicians and patients show that physicians typically

(1) talk significantly more than their patients
(2) provide verbal explanations and information
(3) spend most of their "talk-time" with acknowledgments, questions, and reflections
(4) overestimate the time that patients talk and underestimate the time physicians listen

263. The length of the typical physician-patient interaction time is

(1) not correlated with patient satisfaction
(2) about 15 minutes for office-based specialists
(3) negatively correlated with patient complicance
(4) about 15 minutes for office-based internists

264. Physicians' relationships with their patients are characterized by

(1) support
(2) manipulation of reward
(3) permissiveness
(4) denial of emotional reciprocity

265. Which of the following should be considered essential for effective psychotherapy?

(1) It should be assumed that the sufferer has inherent healing forces that can be mobilized toward further development and well-being
(2) The therapist should focus on awareness that allows differentiation and integration to occur
(3) The therapist should serve as a catalyzer of change
(4) The therapeutic environment should encourage dependency on and trust of the therapist

266. Physicians can help patients change their health-related behavior patterns by

(1) discovering and responding to the patient's personal expectations
(2) simplifying the health treatment plan as much as possible
(3) providing the knowledge to support the recommended behavior
(4) instilling a sense of personal responsibility in the patient for his own health maintenance

SUMMARY OF DIRECTIONS

A	B	C	D	E
1, 2, 3 only	1, 3 only	2, 4 only	4 only	All are correct

267. Common attitudes and feelings of others about cancer patients include which of the following?

(1) Fear they might catch the disease
(2) Tendency to attribute disease to past behavior or undesirable traits of the patient
(3) Fear that discussion about cancer will make the patient uncomfortable
(4) Ambivalent feelings about patients with cancer

DIRECTIONS: Each group of questions below consists of lettered headings followed by a set of numbered items. For each numbered item select the **one** lettered heading with which it is **most** closely associated. Each lettered heading may be used **once, more than once, or not at all.**

Questions 268-272

For each approach to the study of interpersonal behavior below, select the psychologist(s) with whom it is most closely associated.

(A) Solomon Asch
(B) T. Adorno
(C) Leon Festinger
(D) Erving Goffman
(E) John Thibaut and Harold Kelley

268. The authoritarian personality

269. Analysis of roles a person performs

270. Social exchange theory of social interaction

271. Organized central impressions of an individual's traits

272. Theory of cognitive dissonance

Questions 273-275

Match the body language behaviors below with the correct interpretation.

(A) Not willing to enter into a communicative interaction
(B) Closed body position
(C) "I'm interested in you. Notice me"
(D) Assertive and domineering
(E) Submissive and fearful

273. Stroke one's own hair, rearrange clothing, push hair away from face

274. Lower the eyebrows

275. Visually notice someone but then quickly withdraw visual contact

Questions 276-280

Match the statements or descriptions below with the appropriate forms of nonverbal communication.

(A) Facial expressions
(B) Emblems
(C) Illustrators
(D) Self-manipulators
(E) Display rules

276. Movements that amplify or emphasize verbal communications

277. Movements involving one part of the body doing something to another part of the body

278. General universality in occurrence and meaning

279. Body movements that transmit a highly specific message

280. Sex difference in recognition and use

Communication
and Interaction
Answers

247. The answer is A. *(Vander Zanden, ed 4. pp 176-177.)* In the Likert "method of summated ratings" relating to attitude measurement, subjects indicate on five-point scales the extent of their agreement with a series of attitude statements. These ratings are then summated to yield a single attitude score. This technique is less laborious than the Thurstone technique (choice B of the question), in which statements are first sorted by a group of judges into 11 equally spaced categories. The Guttman scalogram (choice E) differs from both of these techniques in that it involves a series of items assumed to be cumulative—that is, acceptance of one statement is assumed to imply acceptance of all other less extreme statements. Whereas Guttman assumes unidimensional concepts, C. E. Osgood argues for multidimensionality. His "semantic differential" (choice D) uses a series of seven-point bipolar scales (e.g., good-bad, strong-weak, active-passive) that are answered with respect to a single word or concept.

248. The answer is E. *(Freeman, ed 3. pp 275-282.)* Doctor-patient interaction studies show that illness makes it difficult or impossible for patients to maintain normal relationships (for example, as parent or employee). Therefore, patients depend on their physicians' competence and knowledge to restore them to good health and to society. Physicians' knowledge, coupled with their patients' dependence, gives them great power, leading patients to recognize doctors as the authorities in the treatment situation. This state of affairs encourages patients to be passive participants in treatment. Such patients may wish to return to a childlike state and to surrender responsibility.

249. The answer is B. *(Counte, pp 65-68.)* Low rates of compliance appear to result from defective relationships between patients and health care providers. The most crucial element in the physician-patient relationship appears to be the nature of role expectations that each has and the congruence and mutuality of such expectations. The exchange of information and facts, similarity of ages, social class differences, and patient rewards are relevant at times but appear to be of less importance than the congruence of expectations between the physician and the patient.

250. The answer is A. *(Froelich, ed 3. pp 36-38.)* Asking a patient "What do you think?" and then correcting or qualifying the answer(s) is an important part of informing a patient or helping the patient to understand the illness and the prospects for the future. It is important to find out what the patient or relative thinks or knows or wants to know about the illness and to give honest answers that will leave the patient or relative with a realistic hope. It is also important to determine the patient's or relative's understanding of what you have discussed and to leave the communication channel open for further questions. A frequent error is for physicians to avoid giving any information or discussing the illness, especially the diagnosis or prognosis, by stating that they prefer not to talk about it until they have all the facts, tests, and so on. Many times the physician is fearful that he or she will only raise the patient's fear or anxiety or appear not to know what the illness is, or perhaps look bad in the patient's eyes by discussing the illness before all the data are in. Yet, the patient and family most often have a whole series of rational and irrational ideas about the illness and its prognosis that should be explored by the physician. The patient must know that the physician will be supportive, regardless of what he or she will be going through.

251. The answer is E (all). *(Allen, pp 97-98.)* David McClelland developed a personal behavior power perspective, emphasizing that behavior can be directed toward individual gain (personal power) or directed toward building the power of a group (socialized power). He also developed the concepts of oppressive power and productive power. Oppressive power is characterized by the aggressive dominance-submission mode with limited effectiveness because it tends to treat others as passive pawns. Productive power involves sharing power so that followers feel powerful and able to accomplish tasks on their own. Power becomes expanded and shared (not given or abdicated). These concepts are particularly relevant to the physician-patient relationship in that the physician who is aware of power dynamics can achieve personal power through oppressive power or socialized power and can achieve productive power by enhancing an alliance and sharing power, which will encourage patients to exercise responsibility and control of their own health.

252. The answer is B (1, 3). *(Counte, pp 97-99.)* The Stanford University community health education study evaluated the relative effects of an intensive multifactor health education campaign on the reduction of cardiovascular risk factors. The study developed a multimedia campaign to encourage people to lose weight, increase exercise, stop smoking, and change their diet. One town was exposed to a large-scale mass media campaign, another received the mass media campaign coupled with behavioral modification training for high-risk individuals, and a third served as a control community. Both test communities decreased cigarette smoking, egg consumption, and cholesterol levels. The community with the mass media campaign plus behavioral modification training achieved the most impressive results. The findings of the study clearly indicate that health beliefs and attitudes can be modified in natural settings as well as in research laboratories. Two problems were emphasized: the powerful countervailing pressures in society that promote smoking and eating of nonnutritional foods and the resistance to change created by the sedentary state of our highly automated society.

253. The answer is A (1, 2, 3). *(Froelich, ed 3. pp 9-12.)* The opening statement in initiating an interview with a patient is important and sets the tone as well as direction of the interview. It is important to learn directly from the patient why he or she has come and to state what you know in a frank and honest manner, recognizing the information the patient has given and encouraging a forthright relationship. The temptation to play the role of an authority may actually inhibit the exchange of information and encourage a dependency role. In general, one must look for interactions that facilitate rather than restrict the interview. Therefore, open-ended rather than yes-or-no questions will usually allow the patient to speak more freely and provide more information.

254. The answer is E (all). *(Froelich, ed 3. pp 55-57.)* All channels of communication between persons other than the literal meaning of words spoken are designated as nonverbal communication. All the following can be considered as nonverbal communication: gesture and posture; touch; dress and grooming; physical distance; facial expression; skin color (e.g., pale, blushing, dehydrated); body hygiene; and even voice inflection, tone, and volume. Nonverbal communications communicate more emotions and feelings than other types of information, but they are important in placing verbal communication into a context. Physicians must be especially sensitive to nonverbal communication in order to secure the maximum communication, information, feelings, and context. It is also important to recognize that differences in cultural and ethnic backgrounds are often expressed in different nonverbal communication patterns.

255. The answer is B (1, 3). *(Vander Zanden, ed 4. pp 89-91.)* Basic emotions, as expressed by facial behavior, are relatively constant across cultures. Of the six basic emotions—happiness, sadness, anger, surprise, disgust, and fear—all the different facial expressions can be recognized and differentiated across cultures except surprise and fear, which appear to be very similar. Even though different cultures establish and teach their own "display rules" that regulate the expression of various emotions, it appears that the central nervous system of humans is genetically pre-wired for the expression of emotions through certain facial behaviors. Thus, the face is a very important vehicle for the nonverbal expression of human experience and emotion.

256. The answer is A (1, 2, 3). *(Leigh, ed 2. pp 27-30.)* Studies of communication between physicians and patients have indicated that patients are generally ready to comply, but less information furnished by the doctor results in less compliance shown by the patient. Many studies have shown that the amount of information provided by physicians results in a higher level of dissatisfaction on the part of the patients than with any other aspect of medical care. Also, expectations are more frequently frustrated by the physician's intentions being too implicit rather than explicit; many problems that arise in communication could be avoided if physicians were more explicit in their communications. There is also considerable evidence that physicians underestimate the desire and ability of lower socioeconomic status patients to handle medical information, so that blue-collar workers and lower socioeconomic status patients tend to be more passive and not to ask questions and hence tend to receive less information than do the upper classes.

257. The answer is A (1, 2, 3). *(Counte, pp 65-68.)* In the interaction between physicians and patients, there are at least three types of problems that typically arise: physicians are often not aware of the emotional impact that "matter-of-fact" statements may make on the patient, often resulting in a high level of anxiety; time constraints and other factors may result in "data overload," where the patient may be presented excessive amounts of information; and technical jargon may produce ambiguity and uncertainty in the patient's mind. The social power of physicians also affects the interaction with patients; decreasing the social distance between the clinician and the patient helps facilitate the therapeutic alliance.

258. The answer is A (1, 2, 3). *(Last, ed 12. p 978.)* Individuals evaluate and make decisions with respect to their symptoms according to a wide variety of influences. In general, two types of variables define an individual's estimate of the impact of these symptoms: perceived seriousness and extent of disruptiveness. Physicians ordinarily focus most on symptoms that have serious implications for the patient's future health status. Patients more often focus on symptoms that tend to interfere in some obvious way with usual activities and routines and on the degree of discomfort rather than the amount or degree of tissue damage.

259. The answer is E (all). *(Mechanic, ed 2. p 407.)* Because patients usually cannot evaluate the abilities and knowledge of their physicians, they tend to base a judgment of professional competence on whether a physician's behavior satisfies their concerns. Thus, physicians' expressed interest in their patients and willingness to give their time to hear the patients' complaints are the usual criteria that patients use in evaluating competence. In addition, self-confidence, a willingness to socialize, and a willingness to make a quick diagnosis and treatment plan are considered by many patients to be indications of a physician's professional competence.

260. The answer is A (1, 2, 3). *(Jaco, ed 3. pp 202-217.)* Hospitalized patients perceive few areas in which they can exercise control, partly because they cannot evaluate the competence of nurses and physicians. In addition, patients fear that exerting control may diminish the quality of care; they express great concern over the need to be cooperative in order to facilitate their recovery, but have little knowledge about specific care and services they should expect or demand. Such patients find that acting the part of consumer with respect to health care—that is, selecting treatment and care they desire—is very difficult, both because they lack technical knowledge and because they perceive the hospital as a crisis institution.

261. The answer is E (all). *(Mechanic, ed 2. pp 407-408.)* How patients evaluate their physicians is determined largely by the degree to which a physician's behavior conforms to a patient's expectations. Physicians whose behavior conforms both to the broad societal definition of appropriate physician behavior and to the expectations of a patient's particular subculture generally will receive high marks. In addition, patients evaluate their physicians on the basis of what they learn from others as well as from their own experience with a physician. The meeting of such expectations can play a major role in patient compliance to prescribed treatment, the likelihood that the patient will return again to the physician, and, to some extent, the potential therapeutic benefits derived from the physician's authority or prestige.

262. The answer is B (1, 3). *(Rosen, pp 231-234, 333.)* Four major empirical studies of verbal interaction between physicians and their patients show similar patterns of interaction. Physicians talked significantly more than patients, even though they believed that they spent much more time listening to their patients. Typically, their utterances were not explanations or communications of information; about two-thirds of what they said were acknowledgments, questions, reflections, and clarifications

263. The answer is A (1, 2, 3). *(Rosen, p 344.)* Physicians frequently claim they are limited by lack of time to spend with patients and patients cite this as one of the most important factors in their decision to change doctors. Yet research does not support this contention. The length of the physician-patient interaction is not correlated with patient satisfaction. Also, there is a negative correlation between the length of the interaction and patient compliance with treatment, with the shorter interactions resulting in higher compliance, and longer interactions yielding lower compliance. A 1979 report indicated that the average time spent with office-based internists was only 8 minutes, and that across specialties the average time was only 15 minutes.

264. The answer is E (all). *(Freeman, ed 3. pp 281-282.)* Talcott Parsons suggests that a physician's relationship to a patient in many respects resembles that of parent to child or of psychotherapist to patient. Physicians provide a strong, stable, nurturant figure on whom a patient may depend; they permit patients to express fears and feelings that would be unacceptable under other circumstances; they reward patients with approval when they try to get well; most of all, they foster an unequal relationship that forbids emotional reciprocity on the physicians' part.

265. The answer is A (1, 2, 3). *(Deci, pp 273-292.)* Effective psychotherapy has been found to include three central ingredients. The first is the assumption that the sufferer has inherent tendencies toward development and well-being that can be mobilized for change. Second, differentiation and integration can occur through a focus on awareness. Finally, the therapist should serve as a catalyzer of change, rather than as a director, or controller, or motivator of change. The therapeutic environment must be informational, encourage independence and autonomous change, and be supportive with positive feedback.

266. The answer is E (all). *(Last, ed 12. pp 1094-1096.)* Physicians have to learn a set of specific educational skills in order to help their patients make significant and lasting changes in their health-related behavior. Several empirical studies have suggested strategies that can be used for improving the effectiveness of health services. Among other strategies the physician should provide continuity of personalized medical care, discover and respond to the patient's expectations in an individualized manner, simplify the health regimen as much as possible, and provide health knowledge that is necessary to support the recommended behavior and is action-oriented. The physician should also make the health behaviors and motives important to the individual and family, maximize the rewards for the prescribed health-related behavior, minimize the cost and inconveniences, try working slowly into regimens that are unpleasant, and instill a sense of personal responsibility in the patient for his or her own health maintenance.

267. The answer is E (all). *(Lindzey, ed 3. pp 823-825.)* Cancer patients generally receive ambivalent responses from others in their own social support networks. Feelings are likely to be negative toward cancer patients and to arouse fear and feelings of their own vulnerability and the possibility they might catch the disease. People are often strongly motivated to protect themselves by attributing the disease to the patient's undesirable characteristics or past behavior. They also fear that any discussion about cancer or death or their negative feelings will make the patient uncomfortable. Therefore, they avoid discussing their feelings and try to assume a "cheerful" role. Under these circumstances, the frequency and quality of the time spent with the patient is most apt to decrease and a certain amount of anxiety is likely to be evoked.

268-272. The answers are: 268-B, 269-D, 270-E, 271-A, 272-C. *(Vander Zanden, ed 4. pp 9-10, 43-45, 186-190, 241, 490.)* Adorno, Frenkel-Brunswik, Levinson, and Sanford developed a theory of the authoritarian personality based heavily on psychoanalytic theory. They postulated that the person with an authoritarian personality has a strong identification with power and also submits to power. They have many mystical explanations for phenomena, and they most often deny their socially unacceptable feelings. In general, they try to explain social interaction on the basis of personality or internal factors rather than on situational factors.

Erving Goffman was a role theorist who attempted to explain social behavior on the basis of a specific role or roles a person enacts to present a certain aspect of oneself. From these role enactments we indicate particular positions we hold or wish to hold. These roles that we learn and enact also help us to facilitate social interactions. He also pointed out that we may learn more about ourselves from these role enactments and from the reactions of other persons to our roles.

John Thibaut and Harold Kelley (also George Homans) are known for their development of the social exchange theory. It is an analysis of interpersonal relations based on S-R (stimulus-response) theory, where complex behaviors are seen as a chain of simpler S-R associations. Social exchange theory provides an account of the contingencies of social interaction in terms of the rewards, costs, outcomes, and comparison levels of interaction sequences. Thus, if the rewards or attractiveness for each participant in an interaction are greater than the costs, the interaction tends to continue. On the other hand, if the costs become greater, then the interaction is terminated.

The Gestalt approach maintains that the whole is greater than the sum of its parts and that social behavior cannot be properly understood if it is separated, analyzed, or reduced to its smallest parts. Thus, social behavior and human experience lose much of their essence and totality if we try to reduce them to specific stimulus-response associations. Asch demonstrated that a list of descriptive characteristics of a person (e.g., intelligent, warm, practical, cautious) is not simply an array of words added together, but that each word relates to the others and creates a total impression that is not conveyed by any single word in the group. Asch placed a strong emphasis on the role of perception in behavior and made other contributions through his study of conformity.

Leon Festinger developed the theory of cognitive dissonance as an outgrowth of the Gestalt framework. Cognitive dissonance deals with the conflict between two beliefs so that when an individual holds two beliefs that are in opposition or inconsistent with each other, the individual is motivated to do something to relieve the dissonance. The cognitive factors can be beliefs, attitudes, or perceived behaviors, and the tension produced by the inconsistency can be relieved or reduced by such actions as adding consonant elements, changing one of the dissonant elements to make it less inconsistent with the other, or perhaps attempting to reduce the importance of the dissonant elements.

273-275. The answers are: 273-C, 274-D, 275-A. *(Vander Zanden, ed 4. pp 84-86.)* A man may straighten his hair or adjust his clothes if he wants to signal "I'm interested in you" or "notice me." Likewise, a woman may stroke her hair, adjust her clothes, check her make-up, or push her hair away from her face. These are called preening behaviors.

If we feel positive toward a person we are more apt to lean toward them, stand closer to them, and look them more directly in the eyes. By looking a stranger in the eyes once or twice, we signal that we are willing to enter into some sort of communicative interaction. If we notice someone, look at them, but then quickly withdraw visual contact, we signal that we are emitting a negative signal that we do not wish to establish a communicative interaction. This has been called civil inattention.

We also perceive the lowering of brows as an assertive and domineering signal and the raising of brows as receptive and submissive.

The closed body position—holding in the elbows, crossing arms, pressing knees together—is a frequent signal emitted by persons who are apt to be angry, hostile, upset, or nonreceptive. In an open body position the elbows are held away from the body, hands and arms are extended outward, legs are stretched out, and one ankle is crossed over the other knee. Physicians must be able to decipher a patient's body language in order to get the full message. Nonverbal patterns signal inner attitudes and feelings, and many researchers conclude that nonverbal clues provide a more salient and valid message than verbal clues.

276-280. The answers are: 276-C, 277-D, 278-A, 279-B, 280-A. *(Baron, ed 4. pp 40-54.)* The ability to read and interpret nonverbal expressions is of critical importance to physicians, since such expressions reveal both intentional and unintentional feelings.

Illustrators are movements that amplify or emphasize words as they are being spoken. These can be movements of the hands to illustrate or emphasize the emotion (e.g., easy or flowing versus jerky or rapid) or they can be facial movements, called speech illustrators, which usually involve the brow, forehead, and eyelids to accent, emphasize, or supply emotion to words being spoken. The type of illustrator used is often related to an individual's ethnic background or culture. Clinically, depressed patients have a low incidence of illustrator usage; as their depression lifts, their use of illustrators increases. Other observations include the following: a decrease in use of illustrators when a patient is attempting to hide his or her feelings; as illustrators decrease, the average voice pitch level increases; and, in general, people who show a high rate of illustrators are regarded by others to be outgoing, sociable, and expressive.

Self-manipulators are movements involving one part of the body doing something to another part of the body. Examples include such movements as scratching one's head, picking one's nose, wringing one's hands, and licking one's lips. They differ from emblems in that they usually occur with little awareness and are not deliberate attempts to convey a message to another person. Also, observing them can be useful to the physician to learn more about a patient, although the message is often diffuse rather than specific. Anxious patients have a high incidence of self-manipulators, and self-manipulators are often regarded as an index of discomfort of a person ill at ease or tense.

Facial expressions, as a form of nonverbal communication, appear to be universal in both occurrence and meaning, particularly in regard to the six basic emotions of happiness, sadness, surprise, fear, anger, and disgust. Cross-cultural studies have demonstrated that people display similar expressions when experiencing a given emotion, even though there are cultural and other learned variations with regard to such dimensions as stoicism or intensity of emotional response that are governed more by display rules and that can mask or conceal universality of facial expressions.

An emblem is a gesture or movement that communicates a specific message or meaning within a given culture. In the United States the following are examples of emblems: crossing the index finger and middle finger as a sign of hope that something will happen or, occasionally, to indicate one is lying; holding the hand upright with the palm outward and fingers together and moving the hand toward another person to indicate "stop"; clenching the fist at shoulder level with elbow bent and moving the hand back and forth toward another person as a sign of protest, anger, or determination to "get even" or aggression toward the other person; forming a circle by joining the end of the thumb and the index finger while holding the arm upright to indicate "OK," or agreement. A wink is considered to be a facial emblem; a head nod "yes" or "no" is a head emblem; a shrug of the shoulders is a body emblem, and so forth. Emblems do vary from culture to culture, but the emotion conveyed is generally clear. One study found less than a hundred emblems for Americans compared with a few hundred for Israelis and Iranians.

A growing body of research demonstrates that women are generally superior to men in both the reading and transmission of nonverbal facial communications. It does not appear to be innate, but is related to certain child-rearing practices in which girls are encouraged to pay attention to nonverbal cues and boys are actively discouraged. When comparing four different types of nonverbal cues (facial expressions, body movements, changes in voice tone, and discrepancies between different nonverbal cues), women were clearly superior in the recognition and use of facial expressions, but showed decreasing superiority with regard to body cues and voice tone, with about equal ability to recognize and use discrepancies.

Group Processes

DIRECTIONS: Each question below contains five suggested responses. Select the **one best** response to each question.

281. According to the Yale studies of attitude change, communicators can increase their persuasiveness by

(A) discussing only one side of an issue when an audience is hostile
(B) presenting only one side of an issue when a competing persuader will get a chance to present the other side
(C) discussing one side of the argument when it is not important to achieve long-lasting attitude change
(D) de-emphasizing their own expertise
(E) allowing an audience of limited intelligence to draw its own conclusions

282. Comparing individual task performance in an isolated environment and in the presence of others, individual task performance is

(A) improved in social situations
(B) impaired in social situations
(C) essentially the same in social and solitary situations
(D) facilitated on easy tasks by the presence of others but impaired by such presence on complex tasks
(E) facilitated on complex tasks by the presence of others but impaired by such presence on easy tasks

283. Social support provides all the following EXCEPT

(A) a mechanism to rely on drugs without guilt
(B) a means for interpretation of situations
(C) the ability for social comparison
(D) models for behavior
(E) access to significant others

284. The view that leadership is a reciprocal process of social influence with leaders and followers being influenced by each other is known as

(A) situational leadership
(B) contingency model
(C) social facilitation
(D) collective behavior model
(E) transactional leadership

285. The most successful primary and secondary prevention strategy against drug abuse has been

(A) an appeal to fear
(B) drug education
(C) affective underpinning
(D) long-term hospitalization
(E) social resistance skills

286. The Hawthorne effect is best illustrated by which of the following situations?

(A) Of a group of factory workers who volunteer for a study of productivity and piecework payment, more than 80 percent quit the project because of the influence of nonvolunteer workers

(B) A group of factory workers who volunteer for such a study demonstrate an improvement in work rate greater than that associated with changed working conditions because they feel specially treated

(C) Work rate increases when workers are allowed frequent brief rest periods

(D) Productivity increases when workers have more opportunity to participate in the organization of their daily routine

(E) Although many workers initially are reluctant to have their routines changed and are suspicious of managerial motives, such changes are quickly accepted if their connection with improved working conditions is demonstrated

287. Recent evidence has indicated that a person in a group will be perceived by its members as a leader if that person's communication is

(A) high in quality, regardless of the quantity

(B) high in quality and low in quantity

(C) high in quality and high in quantity

(D) high in quantity, regardless of the quality

(E) low in quantity, regardless of the quality

288. In order to influence staff nurses who violate infection control policies, an intensive care nurse is more apt to use which of the following social factors?

(A) Legitimate power
(B) Informational power
(C) Coercive power
(D) Referent power
(E) Expert power

289. In the study of group behavior, deindividuation has been found to produce all the following effects EXCEPT

(A) weakened restraints against impulsive behavior
(B) inability to monitor or regulate one's own behavior
(C) decreased sensitivity to immediate cues
(D) lessened concern about evaluations by others
(E) lowered ability to engage in rational planning

DIRECTIONS: Each question below contains four suggested responses of which **one or more** is correct. Select

A	if	**1, 2, and 3**	are correct
B	if	**1 and 3**	are correct
C	if	**2 and 4**	are correct
D	if	**4**	is correct
E	if	**1, 2, 3, and 4**	are correct

290. Accurate statements regarding changes that can occur in individuals' attitudes include which of the following?

(1) Individuals strongly attracted to a group are less likely than other members to change their attitudes in response to facts conflicting with group norms

(2) Individuals are more likely to change a publicly disclosed attitude than a privately held one

(3) Attitude change is more likely to occur if individuals participate in a group discussion than if they listen to lectures

(4) The influence of a group's attitudes on an individual is weakened only if several people openly disagree with the group

291. In order to maintain the support of group members, it is important for a leader to demonstrate

(1) competence in a major group activity

(2) interest in group members and group activity

(3) strong motivation regarding the group and its task

(4) rigorous conformity to group standards

292. Successful leadership is contingent on which of the following?

(1) The leadership style of a particular leader

(2) The interpersonal relationship between leader and followers

(3) The type of task situation in which a leader is involved

(4) The amount of power available to a leader

293. One might expect the socioemotive leader in a group, as opposed to the task leader, to utilize

(1) expert power

(2) coercive power

(3) informational power

(4) referent power

294. Recent studies have demonstrated that intimacy and social networks promote

(1) reduced morbidity

(2) increased longevity

(3) reduced depression

(4) reduced chronic disease

295. Social norms develop by which of the following processes?

(1) Trial and error
(2) Cognitive learning
(3) Conscious intention to achieve the benefits of norms
(4) Chance

296. Effective transmission or maintenance of norms in a group depends on which of the following factors?

(1) Ease of communication within the group
(2) Cohesiveness of the group
(3) Identification of norm violators
(4) Scope of the norm

297. In a group situation, departures from norms are more likely to be tolerated if

(1) the group enjoys strong leadership
(2) the norms have been stated infrequently and vaguely
(3) group members vary widely in age
(4) a dissenting member possesses resources or talents prized by the group

298. Individuals who have social supports

(1) live longer
(2) practice more denial
(3) have fewer somatic illnesses
(4) develop more dependency

299. Studies on attitude change show that individuals are strongly influenced by

(1) comparison of their own attitudes and beliefs with those of others
(2) their own personal and social needs
(3) the need to reduce unpleasant motivational states
(4) persuasive facts and information

DIRECTIONS: The group of questions below consists of lettered headings followed by a set of numbered items. For each numbered item select the **one** lettered heading with which it is **most** closely associated. Each lettered heading may be used **once, more than once, or not at all.**

Questions 300-302

For each theoretical statement or concept, select the investigator(s) with whom it is most closely associated.

(A) Fritz Heider
(B) Daryl Bem
(C) Clark Hull and Kenneth Spence
(D) Kurt Lewin
(E) Leon Festinger

300. People define their attitudes by observing their own behavior. Hence, the best way to change people's attitudes is to change their behavior

301. Having decided between two alternatives nearly equal in attractiveness, a person will find the chosen alternative more attractive and the unchosen alternative less attractive

302. Attitude change is favored when the relations among two persons and an object are unbalanced; resistance to persuasion is more likely to occur when such relations are balanced

Group Processes
Answers

281. The answer is C. *(Middlebrook, ed 2. pp 199-233.)* Hovland, Janis, and Kelley drew a number of conclusions concerning communication effectiveness. For instance, the most effective communicators are those perceived to have both high expertise and credibility. With very intelligent audiences, communicators are more effective if they let their audiences draw their own conclusions; with other audiences, they achieve more attitude change by stating their conclusions explicitly. One-sided arguments are most effective when audiences start out agreeing with the communicator or when there is little chance that an audience will be exposed to the other side of an issue. Although one-sided arguments may be immediately effective, the resulting attitude change is not always enduring. Nevertheless, the studies demonstrated that communicators can increase their persuasiveness by presenting one side of an argument when the audience is generally friendly, or when their position is the only one that will be presented, or when they want immediate, though temporary, opinion change.

282. The answer is D. *(Sears, ed 5. pp 469-471.)* Social facilitation has the effect, in minimal social situations, of improving individual task performance on easy or familiar tasks and of deteriorating performance on more difficult tasks. In general, social facilitation produces an increase in activation levels. Increased arousal level usually results in improved performance on familiar tasks but tends to inhibit the acquisition of new skills or performance on tasks that are complex and unfamiliar.

283. The answer is A. *(Lindzey, ed 3. pp 820-826.)* Studies on the effects of social support have demonstrated that social support provides the ability for social comparison, for interpretation of situations and feelings, and for modeling behaviors, and is a mechanism for access to significant others. Social comparison or social validation provides an important source of information on how others experience the same phenomenon. The social support group helps patients interpret their situation, their feelings, and what is happening to them. Support group individuals in a similar situation can also serve to model behaviors so patients can learn more about the meaning and appropriateness of their own behaviors. Support groups also provide easy access to significant others so that the patient can maintain and enhance personal relationships. Patients without social support are more apt to increase their reliance on drugs or other substances and have less motivation to engage in health-promoting behaviors.

284. The answer is E. *(Baron, ed 4. pp 439-441.)* In the transactional view of leadership, leadership is seen as a reciprocal process of social influence. The leaders are both directing the followers and being influenced by the followers. The focus is on the perception and the relationship between the leaders and followers. Other important considerations in the transactional model are whether followers perceive the leader's position as legitimate or illegitimate, whether leaders perceive their groups in a positive or negative light, and the nature of the task faced by the group. The transactional view is much more complex and interactive than former views, such as the situational view it replaced. The situational theory regarded the task faced by the group and the general situation within which it must operate as the most important factors, rather than the personality traits of the leader or group members as even earlier theories had proposed. The contingency model of leadership analyzes leader effectiveness in terms of two major factors: the leader's personal traits or characteristics and certain features in the situation that play an important role in the leadership process. This model is consistent with the transactional view but attempts to restrict the more fluid components by identifying task-oriented authoritarian leaders and contrasting them with less directive, warm, and relaxed leaders. The situational factors are the leader's personal relationships with other group members, the clarity of the group task, and the power of the leader over the group members. Social facilitation refers to the effects on performance caused by the presence of others; that is, the presence of certain individuals can both facilitate and impair the performance of the group on a particular task. Collective behavior refers to the actions of unrelated persons who happen to be at the same place at the same time, and who are responding to the same stimuli. Examples would be commuters waiting for a bus or train, individuals fleeing a burning building, or persons at the scene of an accident. Under these conditions, group behavior and leadership may be quite different from organized or intentional gatherings.

285. The answer is E. *(Last, ed 12. pp 1080-1086.)* Over the past 25 years, a number of drug abuse prevention programs have been tried. Even though most of them have a high "face validity," the appeal to fear, drug education, attempts to understand our affective selves, and long-term hospitalization have proved to be relatively ineffective in preventing initial or repeated drug dependency and abuse. The teaching of social resistance skills has been more effective than any of the other strategies. The development of general social skills for managing social interactions and overcoming social pressures to use and abuse drugs has shown 35 to 75 percent effectiveness compared (on 2-year follow-up) with 15 to 25 percent for other methods.

286. The answer is B. *(Sears, ed 5. pp 332-335.)* In a piece of classic research at the Hawthorne plant of the General Electric Company, it was found that participation by employees in a special research project had a greater effect on work output than did any of the changes in pay scales, rest periods, and working conditions that the investigators initially wished to study. This phenomenon, in which research participation has greater influence on behavior than do the particular manipulations involved in the investigation, became known as the Hawthorne effect. It suggests that one of the most effective forms of social influence results from making individuals aware that they have been selected for special attention. Such influence is utilized in a wide variety of social investigations, including most forms of experimental research.

287. The answer is D. *(Baron, ed 4. p 441.)* The more actively individuals participate in a group, the more they will be perceived as group leaders. This is found to be true regardless of the quality of participation, apparently because quality and quantity indicate different things to group members. Although quality gives some indication of the ability of the contributor, quantity is seen as an index of motivation. Persons who are regarded as highly motivated toward the group are likely to be perceived as the leaders of the group by its members.

288. The answer is B. *(Eiser, pp 426-436.)* The control of infections acquired in the hospital is still a major problem today. Various social influences are used by intensive care nurses to effect compliance with infection control policies. The social force that is most apt to be used by an intensive care nurse to influence the behavior of staff nurses is informational power (giving the other nurse the reason for the compliance). The use of legitimate power (emphasizing his or her position as an ICN and the other nurse's obligation to comply) and the use of coercive power (warning of possible disciplinary action) are also used, but less frequently than is informational power. Referent power (using other compliers as a frame of reference) and expert power (emphasizing their own superior knowledge or expertise) are used even less frequently. Another finding in the use of social forces to influence individual and group behavior is that staff nurses considered the use of expert power to have the most influence on their own compliance and informational power to be the next most effective. This emphasizes the importance of understanding the power of various social factors to influence individual and group behaviors. A different set of social powers would be more useful in gaining compliance of physicians. For example, referent power is more frequently used than is informational power.

289. The answer is C. *(Baron, ed 4. pp 423-428.)* Deindividuation is a psychological phenomenon that exists in groups where the presence of many other persons appears to weaken the restraints against impulsive or wild behavior, such as destructive vandalism, mob violence, or looting. Their sense of self-awareness is reduced, thus reducing their restraints against impulsive behavior or decreasing their ability to monitor their own behavior. Anonymity, whereby a person feels submerged in a large, undifferentiated group, appears to be the most influential factor leading to a state of reduced self-awareness and deindividuation, thereby allowing the individual to engage in impulsive behavior. Other factors contributing to deindividuation are feelings of close group unity (which act as an external stimulus), a high level of arousal (which can be physiological or emotional), and a focus on external events and goals (which detracts or overpowers internal control and rational behavior). Various studies have demonstrated that the psychological results of deindividuation are a weakened restraint against impulsive behavior, inability to monitor or regulate one's own behavior, a lessened concern for evaluations by others, and a lowered ability to engage in rational planning and other cognitive processes. Studies also show that instead of blocking out or decreasing their sensitivity to immediate cues, as might be expected, people actually experience an increase in sensitivity and reaction to these immediate cues and their current emotional state.

290. The answer is B (1, 3). *(Middlebrook, ed 2. pp 199-233.)* Publicly held opinions are much more resistant to persuasive effects than privately held opinions. In his action-oriented research, Kurt Lewin argued that group discussion and decision-making are much more conducive to attitude change than simply listening to the same information from speakers and lecturers. Solomon Asch's dramatic research on conformity demonstrated that a majority opinion could lead an individual to give erroneous responses on very simple perceptual tasks. However, Asch also showed that this majority power could be considerably weakened by the presence of even a single individual who openly disagreed with the majority. Other investigators studying group influence have shown that members who are most strongly attracted to a group are least likely to be swayed by communications that are inconsistent with group norms.

291. The answer is A (1, 2, 3). *(Hollander, ed 4. pp 478-479.)* A consistent finding in group research is that group members derive particular satisfaction from a leader who demonstrates competence in the group's major activity. There are many kinds of work a leader performs; for example, maintaining interpersonal relationships among group members and striving to keep a group focused on the tasks to be accomplished. Concentrating on the important goals of a group is a major responsibility of the leader. Additionally, it has been found that a leader's commitment and motivation are significantly related to the willingness of members to support their leader. A group's perception of leadership motivation is essential to group function; a leader whose motivation is favorably perceived frequently will be permitted departures from certain group standards.

292. The answer is E (all). *(Middlebrook, ed 2. pp 418-421.)* In his contingency theory of leadership, Fred Fiedler presents three situational factors that are important for predicting both leadership style and who will be an effective leader. Of these factors, he considers leader-group relationships the most important, that is, whether the leader is liked by the members of the group. Another situational factor is the type of task structure—whether the requirements of a situation are clear or ambiguous, for example. To complete the definition of a leadership situation, the power available to a leader must also be determined.

293. The answer is D (4). *(Vander Zanden, ed 4. pp 444-445.)* Exercising influence on the basis of one's status as an expert may further successful completion of the task confronting a group but runs the danger of increasing the social distance between leader and group members, a consequence that would be of more concern to a socioemotive leader than to a task leader. Coercive power may achieve compliance, but only at the expense of a leader's rejection by the group. Informational power, like expert power, also would be more consistent with the task leader's purposes than with the socioemotive leader's, again because of the distancing produced by these power sources. Referent power, by appealing to shared elements among group members, generally tends to promote closer relationships between leader and follower than do the other forms of power. Thus, referent power is the primary form of social power available to a socioemotive leader.

294. The answer is E (all). *(Rosen, p 9.)* Intimacy and social networks have been demonstrated to protect individuals against the occurrence of depression and other morbid conditions. More recently, however, sophisticated studies have also demonstrated a positive effect on longevity. Intimacy and social networks are effective in helping individuals cope with and reduce the effects of chronic disease.

295. The answer is A (1, 2, 3). *(Thibaut, pp 147-148.)* Norms may develop in a number of ways. John W. Thibaut and Harold H. Kelley suggest that norms may be consciously adopted to achieve certain benefits or that they may be adopted by trial and error—whatever works is adopted. Norms also may be imported from similar situations by means of cognitive learning—if situations are parallel, the rules that apply to one apply to the other. Norms do not develop by chance; they develop to meet some need.

296. The answer is E (all). *(Thibaut, pp 240-253.)* Effective norm maintenance and norm transmission (norm-sending) depend on the ease with which group members can communicate. If communication is difficult, transmission of norms is impaired. Norm maintenance also depends on the identification of violators—if violators cannot be identified, sanctions are ineffective. If a norm is universalistic, or applies under virtually all circumstances, it is easier to maintain than if it is particularistic, or applies under limited circumstances. Particularistic norms are more complex and therefore more difficult to transmit. Norms are easier to maintain in cohesive than in noncohesive groups because members are more willing to sacrifice and to submit to sanctions in cohesive groups. Members of noncohesive groups would rather desert than be compelled to comply with group norms.

297. The answer is C (2, 4). *(Thibaut, pp 246-248.)* Group members may wish to ignore a norm if it is burdensome or a source of punishment. Norm rejection is more easily achieved in the absence of enforcement and more readily tolerated if the rejecting member possesses strengths and abilities needed by the group. A norm that has been frequently and clearly stated is more difficult to avoid because members cannot then claim ignorance or misinterpretation. The threat of censure or punishment is a strong deterrent to violation of group norms.

298. The answer is B (1, 3). *(Lindzey, ed 3. p 859.)* Social support serves to buffer and protect healthy and ill individuals from the negative effects of crisis and change. It also helps them with the coping and adaptation process. They live longer, have fewer somatic illnesses, possess higher morale, and have a more positive mental health. The physiological impact of social support appears to affect cardiovascular disease; that is, it appears to affect positively serum cholesterol, catecholamine responses, and severity of coronary artery lesions. Most recently, an association has been found between social support variables and cancer. The pathophysiological mechanisms mediating this relationship are not yet identified. Social support encourages independence and self-confidence and less denial since coping and adaptation are more effective.

299. The answer is A (1, 2, 3). *(Counte, pp 90-93.)* Many studies have been done on the impact of group influences on attempts to change people's attitudes and behavior. These studies view individuals as social beings with considerable dependence on other individuals to provide them with knowledge about the world and about themselves. Persuasive facts and information are not nearly as effective in changing attitudes as are the influence of attempts to satisfy various personal and social needs, the need to reduce unpleasant motivational states, and the process of comparing one's own attitudes and beliefs with those of others. Other group factors that influence attitude and behavior include communicator credibility, communication patterns, and other attributes of the communicator and the situation.

300-302. The answers are: 300-B, 301-E, 302-A. *(Vander Zanden, ed 4. pp 156, 163, 183-185, 186-190, 230.)* Daryl Bem challenged the popular notion that attitudes cause behavior and argued that, actually, the reverse is true. According to Bem's "self-perception" theory, the true cognitive sequence is not "I eat ice cream because I like it" but "I eat ice cream; therefore, I must like it." Hence, it follows that the best way to induce attitude change is to induce behavioral change. Bem's model, which depicts people as coolly and rationally inferring their attitudes from their own behavior, was advanced as an alternative construct for results previously explained by the more motivational theory of cognitive dissonance.

According to Leon Festinger's theory of cognitive dissonance, psychological inconsistency (dissonance) occurs when two or more "cognitive elements" (beliefs, opinions, or bits of knowledge) conflict. This dissonance is unpleasant and motivates an affected person to mitigate it. Thus, when a decision is made between two alternatives that are nearly equally desirable, the negative aspects of the chosen alternative and the positive aspects of the alternative not chosen create dissonance. This dissonance can be reduced by emphasizing the positive aspects of the chosen alternative and the negative aspects of the alternative not chosen. Dissonance can be moderated in other ways, such as trying to downgrade the importance of a decision or revoking the decision completely.

Fritz Heider's balance theory focuses primarily on situations involving two persons and one object. Two kinds of relationships characterize any pair of elements—the liking relation and the unit relation. Each of these relations can be either positive or negative. In a negative liking relation (−), for instance, a person might dislike another object or person. A unit relation is positive (+) when two elements are seen as belonging together (as, for example, when they are members of a set— such as members of a family—or when they are close together physically). If Mary and John were a couple (positive unit relation) and both Mary and John liked professional boxing, a balanced state would exist. If, however, only Mary liked boxing, then the state would be unbalanced, and she or John would be likely to change attitudes about the sport. (Alternatively, they could return to a balanced state by breaking up.) In short, if all three relations among the three elements are positive, or if two are negative and one is positive, the state is a balanced one.

Clark Hull's and Kenneth Spence's extremely influential learning theory inspired several theories of attitude change. According to the Hull-Spence theory, the strength of any response (usually called "excitatory potential" or just "E") is a multiplicative function of four factors: habit strength (H), which is simply the number of times a response has already been produced; drive (D), an overall level of arousal; incentive motivation (K), which is related to the rewards for a response; and inhibitory potential (I), which is related to fatigue.

Family and Community

DIRECTIONS: Each question below contains five suggested responses. Select the **one best** response to each question.

303. All the following statements about fertility and attitudes toward childbearing in the United States are true EXCEPT that

(A) the percentage of young married women who did not plan to have children more than tripled between 1967 and 1973

(B) infertility is personally more serious for women than for men

(C) the age of greatest fertility for women is from 15 to 20 years

(D) in approximately one-third to one-half of infertile marriages it is the man who is sterile

(E) about 10 percent of married couples below the age of 40 will have no children

304. Adolescent delinquency in boys can be predicted most accurately on the basis of

(A) IQ
(B) physique or body type
(C) family size
(D) socioeconomic status of parents
(E) relationship with parents

305. All the following statements about the development of independence during adolescence are true EXCEPT that

(A) sex differences in the age at which independence is achieved tend to be greater in societies whose economy depends on the male's physical strength and motor skills (e.g., hunting and herding versus food-gathering cultures)

(B) compared with the majority of other cultures, independence training in contemporary America begins relatively early but also is relatively protracted

(C) in general, the shift of parental attitudes toward permissiveness that occurs during adolescence is greater in fathers than in mothers

(D) in general, authoritarian parental attitudes are viewed by adolescents as more appropriate in fathers than in mothers

(E) confidence and self-esteem are enhanced by parental attitudes that encourage autonomy yet express interest in an adolescent's behavior and opinions

306. All the following statements about child abuse are true EXCEPT that

(A) fathers abuse their children more often than do mothers
(B) child-abusing parents often were abused by their own parents
(C) prematurely born children are more often abused than are normal-term children
(D) parents are more likely to abuse one "scapegoat" child than to abuse all their children
(E) younger children are more often abused than are older children

307. The most efficacious way to actually reduce automobile accidents and deaths among teenagers is to

(A) provide driver education
(B) raise the legal age for drinking
(C) increase insurance costs (increase the penalty for reckless driving)
(D) raise the legal age for driving
(E) require use of seat belts

308. All the following statements are true about those 75 years of age or older EXCEPT that

(A) 10 percent have never had a child
(B) 68 percent of women are widows
(C) 24 percent of men are widowers
(D) 9 percent of women are divorced or never married
(E) 7 percent of men are divorced or never married

309. The two main functions of the family in America today are which of the following?

(A) Socialization of children and nurturance and security of adult personalities
(B) Achievement of economic security and regulation of sexual behavior
(C) Socialization of children and regulation of sexual behavior
(D) Achievement of economic security and perpetuation of lines of inheritance
(E) Perpetuation of lines of inheritance and stabilization of adult personalities

310. The most consistent parental behavior found in cases of child abuse is

(A) inconsistency in discipline
(B) employment of harsh mental punishment
(C) rejection
(D) parents treating the child as they were treated by their parents
(E) persuasiveness

311. Research results show that all the following statements are true EXCEPT that

(A) married persons have a significantly longer life expectancy than nonmarried persons, especially when compared with formerly married persons

(B) separated or divorced men have a much higher admission rate to state and county psychiatric hospitals than do married men

(C) widowed women have a higher admission rate to state and county psychiatric hospitals than do widowed men

(D) widowed women have a higher admission rate to state and county psychiatric hospitals than do separated or divorced women and never-married women

(E) death rates for heart disease and cancer of the respiratory tract are twice as high for divorced white men compared with married white men

312. Ethnocentrism is the

(A) belief that ethnic groups should remain geographically segregated

(B) tendency to think that one's own group or way of life is preferable or superior

(C) belief that ethnic groups should not intermarry

(D) belief that values held by marriage partners should be in accord

(E) belief that multiple cultural practices should be incorporated into marriage and the family

313. Absence of the father in the home has all the following effects on children EXCEPT that

(A) it has a more detrimental influence on the child's personality in early development than when the absence occurs after 5 years of age

(B) for male children, absence of the father because of divorce, separation, or desertion is not as detrimental as absence because of death

(C) for female children, the earlier the absence of the father, the more mothers are apt to display overprotection

(D) in cases of absence of the father because of divorce, adolescent girls actively and aggressively seek the attention of men

(E) in cases of absence of the father because of death, the reaction of adolescent girls is active avoidance of male peers and a preference for other girls as companions

314. The percentage of married women who were employed rose from 5.5 percent in 1900 to what percentage in 1978?

(A) 21 percent
(B) 31 percent
(C) 41 percent
(D) 51 percent
(E) 61 percent

315. The most common reason for cohabitation outside of marriage is

(A) temporary convenience
(B) trial marriage
(C) permanent alternative to marriage
(D) overt and covert rebellion
(E) experimentation with a new life-
     style

DIRECTIONS: Each question below contains four suggested responses of which **one or more** is correct. Select

A	if	**1, 2, and 3**	are correct
B	if	**1 and 3**	are correct
C	if	**2 and 4**	are correct
D	if	**4**	is correct
E	if	**1, 2, 3, and 4**	are correct

316. Persons tend to marry others who are similar to themselves rather than different from themselves with regard to which of the following characteristics?

(1) Intelligence
(2) Nationality
(3) Family background
(4) Previous marital status

317. Which of the following hypotheses can account for reported inconsistencies between the attitudes people express and their actual behavior?

(1) Attitudes often are measured very imprecisely
(2) Norms, expectations, and situational demands can alter people's readiness to behave in accordance with their attitudes, while leaving unchanged the basic underlying attitude
(3) Attitude questionnaires often measure orientation toward some general category, whereas behavioral assessments often involve only one facet of that category
(4) Attitudes and behavior are reciprocally influential

318. Effective parental discipline of children requires

(1) consistency—no significant change in expectations through time
(2) follow-through—parental attention to the child's response to discipline
(3) immediate feedback—the quicker the consequences of an action are experienced, the more learning takes place
(4) self-disclosure—children need to know that parents are human and make mistakes

319. Women with high rates of heavy drinking include

(1) young women with small children
(2) women with alcoholic husbands
(3) employed women in stressful occupations
(4) women in the presence of men

320. The loss of a mate is most often followed by a loss of

(1) social validation
(2) task performance
(3) social support
(4) social protection

321. Research on the relationship between marital success and the birth order of the partners shows that

(1) first-born male and later-born female partnerships have high marital success

(2) first-born male and first-born female partnerships have low marital success

(3) youngest male and youngest female partnerships have low marital success

(4) later-born male and first-born female partnerships have low marital success

322. A greater likelihood of marital adjustment and stability exists

(1) the lower the social class of the couple

(2) the younger the couple are when they marry

(3) if the two are of different levels of intelligence

(4) the higher the educational level of the couple

323. Daughters of mothers who were employed during some period of the daughters' childhood or adolescence tend to

(1) aspire to a career outside the home

(2) aspire to more advanced education

(3) get better grades in college

(4) have less stereotyped views of female roles

324. An early study by Pauline Bart looked at the "empty nest" syndrome. Subsequent studies of this syndrome have shown that women who have launched their last child report

(1) a less meaningful existence

(2) more feelings of depression

(3) less positive self-concepts

(4) less stress

DIRECTIONS: Each group of questions below consists of lettered headings followed by a set of numbered items. For each numbered item select the **one** lettered heading with which it is **most** closely associated. Each lettered heading may be used **once, more than once, or not at all.**

Questions 325-328

Select the type of parental behavior that would be expected to result in each of the types of children characterized below.

(A) Cold-rejectance with autonomy-permissiveness
(B) Warmth-acceptance with autonomy-permissiveness
(C) Cold-rejectance with control-restrictiveness
(D) Warmth-acceptance with control-restrictiveness
(E) None of the above

325. Dependent, extremely cooperative with peers and adults, does not show extreme behaviors

326. Acting out behaviors, rebelliousness, and patterns of delinquence

327. Passive, shy, follower, anxious to win approval of peers and adults

328. Self-centered child, often "spoiled," inadequate impulse control, relationships with peers impaired

Questions 329-332

For each list of personality characteristics, select the birth-order position with which it is closely associated.

(A) Oldest child
(B) Middle child
(C) Youngest child
(D) Only child
(E) None of the above

329. Conceptual thinker, ambitious, quick-tempered, prefers leadership positions, parent-oriented, peacemaker

330. Affectionate, carefree, entertaining, most likely to become alcoholic, may feel very inferior, wastes time

331. Competitive, friendly, peer-oriented, self-confident, practical, accepts advice easily, adaptable to others, sociable, poor loser

332. Interested in heritage, independent, self-centered, academically oriented, difficulty in sharing, parent-oriented

Questions 333-336

The ethnic background of the family may have a significant influence on children's school success. For each pattern of school performance, select the ethnic background with which it is most closely associated.

   (A) Black
   (B) Jewish
   (C) Chinese
   (D) Hispanic
   (E) Native American

333. Children tend to show good verbal abilities but relatively poorer numerical scores

334. Children tend to show consistent high skills in reading, numerical, and spatial activities, but poorer performance in verbal areas

335. Children tend to show more skill in verbal tasks and poorer performance on problems of reasoning and spatial relations

336. Children tend to perform better on spatial-related tasks and more poorly on verbal ability tasks

Family and Community Answers

303. The answer is C. *(Bell, ed 6. pp 393-406.)* Ultimately, about 10 percent of all couples will have no children. In the 1960s only about 1 percent of all couples preferred to remain childless; however, between 1967 and 1973 the proportion of wives who stated they did not expect to have children more than tripled from 1.3 percent to 4 percent. There is also strong evidence that those who do have children will have fewer in the future. For example, one study showed that in 1968 41 percent of the public declared their ideal number of children to be four or more, whereas by 1974, the ideal of four or more children had decreased to only 19 percent. Fertility problems and the possibility of not having children are more personally serious for women than for men because the mother role is more basic to their sense of self. Until recently, it has been generally assumed that the inability to conceive was the "fault" of the woman; however, it is now estimated that about one-third to one-half of all infertile marriages are due to the sterility or other problems of the man. The fertility rate in both women and men is related to age. Women reach their highest potential fertility from about age 18 to age 25. After the mid-20s there is a gradual decline in fertility until age 35, when there is a sharper decline to age 49. Male fertility also declines with age, but the decline is not as rapid or as definite.

304. The answer is E. *(Conger, ed 3. pp 623-625.)* The nature of an adolescent boy's relationship with his parents is the single factor most predictive of juvenile delinquency. In the most extensive study of the subject, J. G. Bachman found that the better a boy reported he got along with his parents, the less likely he was to engage in delinquent behavior. Other studies have found that delinquency is related to overly severe and overly lax home discipline as well as to an atmosphere of mutual hostility and rejection between parents and children. Despite the widely held belief that most delinquents come from broken homes, recent evidence indicates that the incidence of delinquency among boys of unhappy, though intact, homes is greater than that among boys of broken homes.

305. The answer is C. *(Conger, ed 3. pp 224-254.)* Most societies stress independence more in male than in female adolescents; however, the sex difference is greatest in hunting and herding cultures. Independence training in American culture begins early but is prolonged, leading to the phenomenon that Erik Erikson has termed the "psychosocial moratorium." In contemporary America, parents usually shift toward more permissive attitudes as their child matures; however, this shift is more pronounced in mothers than in fathers.

306. The answer is A. *(Kaplan, ed 4. pp 591-592, 838-839.)* Certain children are singled out for abuse by their parents; these children frequently were born prematurely and were slower to develop than were their siblings. Child abuse is committed most often on children below the age of 3. A principal finding in studies of the personality of parents who abuse their children is that such parents usually were abused by their own parents. Mothers abuse their children more often than do fathers, probably because mothers have more contact with their children.

307. The answer is D. *(Rosen, p 16.)* While behavior change is most often the most effective means of promoting health, technological or regulatory measures can be more successful in certain instances. If the goal is to reduce automobile accidents and deaths among teenagers, raising the legal age for driving is more effective than driver's education or encouraging the use of seat belts. Raising the legal age for drinking or adding punitive insurance costs will have some reducing effect, but not as much as raising the legal age for driving. An aggregate strategy of mixing education, technology (safety devices), and regulation is the most effective.

308. The answer is A. *(Andres, pp 180-181.)* A significant number of the elderly do not have a close family member on whom they can rely. Sixty-eight percent of women and 24 percent of men at the age of 75 or older are widowed. In addition, 9 percent of the women and 7 percent of the men are divorced or have never married. Add to this the 20 percent of the 65-and-older population who have never had a child and an increasing number who have outlived their children, and it becomes apparent that the elderly do not have the family resources to help them in failing health. Neighbors and friends can help but do not approach the level of help of family.

309. The answer is A. *(Bell, ed 6. pp 3-17.)* The American family has progressively lost a number of its previous functions, such as educating its offspring and serving as a center of recreational activity. Two major functions are left to the family: socialization of offspring and stabilization of adult personalities. The influence of parents during their children's early years suggests that socialization is still one of the family's primary functions, despite the fact that other agencies (e.g., schools) have taken over some aspects of this task. The second function, that of stabilization of adult personalities, is accomplished when men and women succeed in adjusting themselves to roles of parental responsibility and sharing nurture and security. The changes occurring in marriage, women's roles, child care, divorce, and remarriage do not necessarily affect the family adversely.

310. The answer is A. *(Lerner, 1983. pp 295-297.)* Studies on child abuse have found that inconsistency in discipline is the most frequent parental behavior in virtually every instance. Also, abusive parents often use harsh physical punishment in controlling their children. Another repeatedly observed finding is that abusive parents tend to have been abused by their own parents. This creates a generation effect whereby the harsh discipline practices of one generation may serve as a model for the next generation. Thus physicians attempting to work with cases of child abuse should focus on breaking the cycle of parental behaviors for one generation. Many child-abusive parents may be rejecting and cold toward their children, but they are more apt to be overcontrolling rather than permissive.

311. The answer is C. *(Last, ed 12. pp 957, 986.)* There are significant relationships between marital status and health status. The married have a significantly longer life expectancy than the nonmarried, especially when compared with the formerly married (widowed, divorced, or separated). Married persons have less chronic illness, especially mental illness, than the formerly married and make fewer requests for health care service. Children raised in single-parent families have more illness and make more demands on the health care service system than children in families where both parents are present. Death rates comparing divorced and married white men show that divorced white men have twice as many deaths from heart disease and cancer of the respiratory tract as married white men. Separated or divorced men have a higher admission rate to state and county psychiatric hospitals. Widowed men have a higher admission rate to state and county psychiatric hospitals than do widowed women, but widowed women have a higher admission rate than separated or divorced women and never-married women.

312. The answer is B. *(Vander Zanden, ed 4. pp 409-410.)* Ethnocentrism is the tendency to consider one's group, or way of life, usually national or ethnic, superior to other groups and to use one's own group as the frame of reference against which other groups are judged. Americans are sometimes considered ethnocentric because of the relative isolation of American families from persons of different cultures and their ways of life. This can often cause us to have a very narrow view of marriage and family life.

313. The answer is B. *(Lerner, 1986. pp 596-598.)* Research on factors that influence children's personality development has often been directed at studying the effects of the absence or withdrawal of specific factors. Thus, to understand the effects of the absence of the father from the home, situations of separation, desertion, divorce, or death have been studied. Results have shown that the effect on the child's personality depended on the sex of the child and the timing of and the reason for the father's absence. A father's absence during a child's early development has a more detrimental effect than when the absence occurs after the child is 5 years old. For males, the absence of the father caused by death is not as detrimental as absence caused by divorce, separation, or desertion. For females, absence of the father caused by death seemed to interfere more with overall adjustment than for males. Absence of the father alters the interaction of adolescent girls with other males, producing one of two extreme reactions. In cases of absence caused by divorce, girls actively and aggressively seek social and physical attention of men. In cases of absence caused by death, however, girls are more apt to react with avoidance of male peers and a preference for other girls as companions. Other studies have shown that the absence of fathers from either divorce or death caused girls to express more insecurity about their ability to relate to males: divorce more often led to overinvolvement, and death typically led to avoidance. Also, the earlier the absence of the father had occurred, the more mothers were likely to have displayed overprotection. Other studies of boys with absent fathers showed a tendency for conflict and uncertainty as to appropriate masculine orientations—sometimes resulting in a "supermacho" role as overcompensation, and in other instances a more feminine orientation.

314. The answer is D. *(Lerner, 1986. pp 598-601.)* From 1900 to 1978, the percentage of all adult women (age 20 to 64) in the labor force rose from 20 to 58 percent. The percentage of married women who were employed rose from 5.5 percent in 1900 to 51 percent in 1978. Black women are more likely than are white women to work outside the home, and this difference is maintained across various educational levels. Since the proportion of women in professional graduate schools is increasing rapidly, the future complexion of the work force will certainly be altered. Yet, despite these continuing changes and the increase of women in the work force, the vocational role orientations of females and of males remain more traditional than one would expect. This too is expected to change as the proportion of women in the work force increases.

315. The answer is A. *(Kammeyer, pp 160-178.)* Cohabitation, usually defined as an unmarried male and an unmarried female living together, has become more frequent in recent years. It is especially evident on college and university campuses (where most of the research on this phenomenon has been conducted), but it is also becoming more common in other communities in the United States. The most frequent reason for cohabitation is as a temporary matter of convenience or choice without any necessary commitment to marriage. The second most frequent reason given for cohabitation is as a "trial marriage" in which couples may anticipate marriage but live together to test compatibility or to await more favorable personal circumstances for marriage. Another reason for cohabitation is as a permanent and lasting alternative to marriage. Although cohabitation generally involves persons in their late teens and in their twenties, increasing numbers of individuals in their thirties and forties are cohabitating, particularly after a divorce or separation. Overt or covert rebellion plays a role in a small minority of cohabitations, as does experimentation with a new life-style, but the predominant motivations are as a temporary matter of convenience or choice of individuals involved in an affectional relationship.

316. The answer is E (all). *(Kammeyer, pp 246-247.)* Persons tend to marry others who are similar to themselves, a principle called homogamy. Homogamy is the norm in mate selection. Strong evidence indicates that Americans prefer mates who are similar to rather than different from themselves, contrary to the conventional wisdom in our culture stating that "opposites attract." The most important social characteristics in which mates prefer similarity are age, nationality, race, family background, education, intelligence, previous marital status, and religion. Many social forces encourage homogamy, such as attending the same high school or college and parental opposition to or acceptance of a particular religion. Despite the tendency to homogamy, there are still many marriages among persons of dissimilar social backgrounds. Many such "mixed" marriages are quite successful. Each individual person's personal qualities and total adjustment are still more important than elements of similarity or difference.

317.   The answer is E (all). *(Vander Zanden, ed 4. pp 174-182.)* For many reasons, attitudes are never measured precisely. For example, test items may be ambiguous, or respondents may attempt to describe themselves in more favorable, rather than more accurate, terms. Behavior may be consistent with attitudes if situational norms and expectations favor consistency, but not if they do not. Researchers often use questionnaires that tap attitudes toward some general category, but measure behavior toward only one aspect of that category. Thus, a researcher might devise a scale to measure attitudes toward blacks, then ask respondents to pose for a picture with a specific black person. In a recent discussion of the attitude-behavior controversy, H. A. Alker has suggested that consistency may itself be an individual variable— that is, some people may show more consistency between attitude and behavior than others. In general, attitudes influence and are influenced by three components: the cognitive, the affective, and the behavioral.

318.   The answer is E (all). *(Schuster, ed 2. pp 373-374.)* The most effective parental discipline of children uses several basic principles that apply in all situations to all children. If properly used, these principles help children by guiding them toward the goal of becoming self-actualized, self-directed, socialized adolescents and adults. Parental expectations must be consistently maintained through time. The principle of follow-through entails parental attention to the child's response to discipline. If a certain form of disciplinary punishment is stated, then it must be carried through. Discipline should be paced with the maturational level of the child. The quicker the consequences of an action are experienced, the more learning takes place. This is the principle of immediate feedback. Delayed consequences are usually ineffective in changing behavior. Adults must be truthful with children at all times. Effective child-rearing practices involve mutual trust. Children need to feel that their parents are human and fallible just as they are. They need to know that parents often can and do make mistakes. The most important principle of discipline is genuine love. Adults and parents who really love their children rarely fail in raising autonomous, socialized, self-actualizing children. Genuine love is not an accident; it must be learned and pursued.

319. The answer is A (1, 2, 3). *(Braunwald, ed 11. p 2108. Rosen, p 39.)* Studies of the drinking habits of women have found that the highest rates of heavy drinking are among young women with small children, women with alcoholic husbands, and employed women, especially women in stressful occupations. On the average, women tend to drink less than men, but in the presence of men they tend to drink even less. Effects of high ethanol intake particular to women include amenorrhea, decreased size of ovaries, absence of corpora lutea with associated infertility, and spontaneous abortion.

320. The answer is E (all). *(Lindzey, ed 3. pp 823-825.)* There is an increase in mortality following the loss of a mate and the subsequent bereavement. The loss of a partner leads to a deficit in the areas of social validation, social support, task performance, and social protection. The loss of social validation means loss of important information in terms of confidence of one's own judgments, assessments, and appropriateness of ideas and behavior. The survivor also recognizes the loss of routine and special tasks that were provided and given by the deceased. The loss of social support and unconditional positive regard seriously reduces a major source of self-esteem and self-regard. Not only is there a great deal of disruption, but it often fosters a sense of helplessness.

321. The answer is A (1, 2, 3). *(Schuster, ed 2. pp 352-353.)* Research indicates that the combination of birth orders of partners in terms of marital success is as follows: high marital success is associated with first-born male and later-born female, later-born male and first-born female, and middle-born male or female and any birth order. Medium marital success is associated with only child, male or female, with first-born. Low success is associated with first-born male and first-born female, youngest male and youngest female, and only child male and only child female. Obviously, birth order is only one of many factors involved in adjustment to adulthood and to marriage, but it is important to recognize that children within the same family have different social learning experiences and differential reinforcement of behavior patterns, which, among other factors, can foster independence, leadership, dependence, or other characteristics and interpersonal skills.

322. The answer is D (4). *(Kammeyer, pp 245-247.)* There is a greater likelihood of poor adjustment in marriage and higher potential for subsequent divorce the younger people are when they marry. When women marry in their teens and men marry under the age of 22, they are about twice as likely to obtain a divorce as persons who marry when they are older. In general, the lower the social class of persons marrying, the less stable the marriage. Persons from upper-class backgrounds are more apt to have marriages that are better adjusted and less prone to divorce, possibly reflecting higher financial resources. Also, the higher the educational level, the greater the marital adjustment and stability. A higher educational level is also correlated with a later age at marriage and a higher income. Marital stability appears to be negatively affected when the education level of the wife is higher than that of the husband. Difference in intelligence and difference in education are not necessarily concomitant as lack of education is not proof of lack of intelligence. The dangers of differences in intelligence are that the partners may grow apart, intellectual isolation may be unsatisfying to the one with superior intelligence, and they may discover that intellectual stimulation and exchange of ideas can be as important as emotional and physical stimulation.

323. The answer is E (all). *(Lerner, 1983. pp 573-574.)* One of the most consistent and well-documented correlates of career orientation departure from traditional feminine roles is maternal employment during childhood and adolescence. Daughters of mothers who were employed during some period of the daughters' childhood or adolescence generally aspire to a career outside the home, aspire to more advanced education, get better grades in college, and have less stereotyped views of female roles than do daughters of nonworking mothers. Also, daughters of working mothers are more apt to choose a traditionally masculine occupation than those of nonworking mothers. Daughters of working mothers have a broader definition of the female role and are more likely to emulate their mothers and more often name their mother as the person they aspire to be like. Working mothers also appear to promote independence rather than dependency in their daughters. Thus, it has been shown that family settings having particular characteristics can promote the development of vocational roles that vary from the traditional.

324. The answer is D (4). *(Atchley, ed 4. pp 120-121.)* An earlier study by Pauline Bart argued that the role of full-time mother leaves women in a difficult and depressed state when their children reach adulthood and leave home. This was designated as the "empty nest" syndrome. Subsequent studies have shown that this conventional wisdom is misleading; that women report less stress; that many newlyweds visit or telephone their parents, use their cars, and so on; that with delayed marriage, getting children to leave home is becoming a bigger problem; that middle-aged women who had not launched their children reported much less positive self-concepts than those who had, especially in interpersonal relationships; and that, in general, women look forward to the freedom and opportunity acquired by having their children launched. The increase in divorce at this age is more often related to the departure's unmasking of an empty marriage than to the empty nest syndrome.

325-328. The answers are: 325-D, 326-A, 327-C, 328-B. *(Lerner, 1983. pp 282-285.)* Most parental behavior can be categorized somewhere between the four extremes of warmth-acceptance versus cold-rejectance and autonomy-permissiveness versus control-restrictiveness. In general, warm-accepting parents provide understanding and emotional support, respond positively to a child's appropriate behaviors, express physical affection, and provide an explanation for their disciplinary actions. The cold-rejecting parent demonstrates the opposite behaviors. Restrictive-controlling parents typically impose a large number of rigidly enforced rules involving almost every aspect of the child's behavior. They expect obedience, no back talk, and no aggression. Autonomy-permissive parents are the opposite. Most parental behavior can be categorized as a combination of these more extreme positions. Various studies have found that when the more extreme cold-rejectance is combined with autonomy-permissiveness the children are more apt to show acting out behaviors, rebelliousness, and patterns of delinquency. They also are apt to be "loners," immature, and have emotional problems thought to result from excessive freedom, noncaring parents, and feelings of rejection.

Combining warmth-acceptance with autonomy-permissiveness is more apt to result in children who are self-centered and "spoiled" and who have inadequate impulse control and impaired ability to get along with their peers. This is thought to result from combining freedom with emotional concern, love with an unwillingness to set limits for their children.

Cold-rejectance with control-restrictiveness is associated with conforming and submissive children who are more passive, shy, and anxious to win and maintain approval of peers and adults. The children do not feel warmly loved or accepted by their controlling and distant parents and do not appear to develop the independence and self-sufficiency they need to be leaders rather than followers.

Combining warmth-acceptance with control-restrictiveness produces many of the characteristics described for cold-rejectance with control-restrictiveness, except that the children perceive their parents as loving and concerned, but perhaps too overprotective, leading to dependence and extreme cooperation with peers and adults. They are often regarded as model children, not too compliant or too rebellious, too loud or too quiet, just moderate, but not generally independent or creative.

Most authorities stress that parents should provide an atmosphere of warmth-acceptance coupled with moderate autonomy-permissiveness that would allow and foster traits of responsibility, self-initiative, achievement, goal direction, and independence. Another generalization from research is that inconsistency of parental discipline has a detrimental influence on a child's personality and social development.

329-332. The answers are: 329-A, 330-C, 331-B, 332-D. *(Schuster, ed 2. p 344.)* Research on the relationship between personality characteristics and birth order shows that there is a tendency for certain personality clusters associated with the positions of oldest child, youngest child, middle child, and only child.

The oldest child tends to be anxious and fearful, tends to be a peacemaker, matures early, is a conceptual thinker, prefers leadership positions, seeks signs of appreciation, is interested in heritage, and is honest, serious, parent-oriented, ambitious with high goals, and quick-tempered or easily angered.

The youngest child tends to be lazy, wastes time, makes excuses, is dependent, may feel quite inferior, is most likely to become an alcoholic, and is affectionate, lower in academic achievement, creative, carefree, and entertaining.

A middle child tends to be competitive, a poor loser, a good leader, friendly, peer-oriented, self-confident, realistic, self-accepting, most adaptable to others, popular with peers, practical, and sociable, has realistic goals, and accepts advice readily.

An only child tends to be a conceptual thinker, is interested in heritage, has difficulty in sharing and is a loner, and is parent-oriented, anxious and fearful, academically oriented, independent, honest, self-centered, and critical.

333-336. The answers are: 333-A, 334-C, 335-B, 336-D. *(Lerner, 1983. pp 236-243.)* In our society, one of the best predictors of school success is the family's position in the social structure. Middle-class children are much more successful in school than are children from the lower social classes. The ethnic background of the family may have a significant influence on children's school success. On studying verbal abilities, general reasoning skills, numerical abilities, and spatial relations skills of Chinese, black, Jewish, and Hispanic first-grade children, it was found that Chinese children tend to show consistent high skills in reading, numerical, and spatial tasks but poorer performance in verbal areas. Black children tend to show good verbal abilities but relatively poorer numerical abilities. Jewish children tend to show more skill in verbal tasks and poorer performance on problems of reasoning and spatial relations. Hispanic children tend to perform better on spatial relations and poorer on verbal ability tasks.

Sociocultural Patterns

[handwritten: Fascism is a measure of authoritarian personality]

DIRECTIONS: Each question below contains five suggested responses. Select the **one best** response to each question.

337. *[handwritten: authoritarian]* The F-scale developed by Theodore Adorno and coworkers was intended to be a measure of

(A) fear
(B) fixation
(C) frustration
(D) fascism
(E) none of the above

338. Biological responses are most adversely influenced over time by

(A) regressiveness
(B) interpersonal conflict
(C) confusion
(D) uncontrollability
(E) fearfulness

339. An important therapeutic aspect of curanderismo often lacking in Western scientific medicine is the

(A) ability to "cure" psychosomatic illnesses
(B) cultural congruence between healer and patient
(C) extensive use of symbolism
(D) laying on of hands
(E) use of herbal preparations

340. A social norm is best defined as

(A) a rule
(B) average behavior
(C) one individual's expectations of another
(D) shared expectations about behavior
(E) recommended behavior

341. An effective strategy for maintaining a strong relationship between employee performance and employee satisfaction is to

(A) give all employees equal raises
(B) pay all employees what they are worth in the marketplace
(C) pay all employees more than they are worth in the marketplace
(D) pay good performers much more than poor performers
(E) pay good performers slightly more than poor performers

342. Which of the following statements about a system for controlling the output of members of an organization is true?

(A) It is not an essential component of an organization
(B) It is trusted more by employees if it involves subjective judgments of performance rather than objective measures
(C) It cannot depend alone on social pressure on its members to conform
(D) It may induce behavior that fails to contribute to overall organizational goals
(E) It is more effective when set by someone other than the individuals affected by it

343. The most effective method of reducing racial prejudices is through

(A) interracial contact
(B) introducing black studies into elementary school curricula
(C) psychotherapy for black-white confrontations
(D) improving the black image in the mass media
(E) legislating against prejudiced behavior

344. Considering the characteristics of the population over age 65, all the following statements are true EXCEPT that

(A) the older population has been getting larger
(B) the older population is expected to level off in numbers by the year 2000
(C) about 5 percent are residents of nursing homes
(D) the female population has increasingly outnumbered the male population
(E) of the 85-and-older segment, the number of men per 100 women is expected to decrease from about 45 to about 39 by the year 2000

345. An individual becomes more vulnerable to the condition of psychological and physical distress if he or she is

(A) aware of diagnostic test results
(B) given patient education
(C) denying the illness
(D) introspective
(E) receiving counseling

346. Studies of pain response among different American ethnic groups disclosed that, for disorders of equivalent objective severity, the degree of open and vocal response to pain was greatest in which of the following groups?

(A) "Old American" and Jewish
(B) Italian and Jewish
(C) Irish and "Old American"
(D) Jewish and Irish
(E) Italian and "Old American"

347. In comparing alcohol consumption in women and men, each of the following is true EXCEPT that (9 more)

(A) women and men who are heavy drinkers are equally susceptible to alcohol-related morbidity and mortality
(B) the cost to society of comparable alcoholism levels is greater for women
(C) in mixed company, women drink less
(D) the amount of alcoholism among men is greater
(E) social norms display less tolerance of heavy drinking in women

348. Ethnic differences in response to pain are attributable primarily to

(A) differences in pain threshold
(B) differences in subjective experience of pain
(C) intellectual ability to grasp the significance of a disease
(D) cultural traditions of stoicism or emotionalism
(E) experimental bias

349. All the following statements about teen-age use of alcohol are true EXCEPT that 7 6 °6

(A) 80 percent of teenagers (12 to 17 years of age) report having tried alcohol
(B) since 1966, the number of high school students who report they become intoxicated at least once a month has doubled from 10 to over 20 percent
(C) more than 30 percent report they drink alcohol once or twice a week
(D) 3 percent of male high school seniors report they drink alcohol each day
(E) nearly 80 percent of male high school seniors report that they drink at least once a month

350. The basic symbol of Chinese-American medicine is the

(A) mandarin hat and coat
(B) dragon
(C) dog
(D) yin yang
(E) snake

351. In Talcott Parsons's formulation of the "sick role," which of the following statements is true?

(A) The sick person has the right to refuse to cooperate in the process of getting well
(B) The sick person has the right to be defined as "not responsible" for his or her condition
(C) The sick person has the right to take advantage of any secondary gains involved in being sick
(D) The sick person has the right but not the obligation to define the state of being sick as undesirable
(E) None of the above

352. Among spiritual healers, the most common theory of disease is that

(A) disease is a spiritual malaise resulting from sinful acts
(B) disease results from psychological stress
(C) disease is caused by parapsychological phenomena
(D) disease is caused by germ-mechanical factors
(E) disease is caused by invasion of the body by evil spirits

353. According to nutritional experts, Americans should modify their eating habits to improve their level of health. All the following activities are recommended EXCEPT to

(A) increase the percentage of protein intake
(B) decrease the percentage of total fat intake
(C) increase the carbohydrate intake
(D) decrease the intake of saturated fats
(E) increase the intake of complex carbohydrates

DIRECTIONS: Each question below contains four suggested responses of which **one or more** is correct. Select

A	if	**1, 2, and 3**	are correct
B	if	**1 and 3**	are correct
C	if	**2 and 4**	are correct
D	if	**4**	is correct
E	if	**1, 2, 3, and 4**	are correct

354. Patients who are ill and facing death exhibit reactions to the loss of

(1) independence
(2) self-image
(3) control
(4) financial resources

355. Dieting induced by social and cultural pressures results in

(1) a lowered basal metabolic rate
(2) hormonal changes that promote fat storage afterwards
(3) plateaus in the process of weight loss
(4) increasingly compulsive strategies in the pursuit of an ideal weight

356. A patient is less apt to comply with a physician's recommendations if the treatment

(1) interferes with the patient's personal behavior
(2) is rather complex
(3) is long term
(4) is expensive

357. Which of the following variables will influence a bystander's decision to help in an emergency?

(1) Distance from the other person
(2) Knowledge of what to do
(3) Size of the group in the immediate area
(4) Bystander's gender

358. In aging, adapting to lost roles or activities is accomplished by which of the following approaches?

(1) Consolidation
(2) Disengagement
(3) Substitution
(4) Disorganization

359. An organization whose employees are satisfied with their pay relative to what they could earn in another organization, but dissatisfied with their pay relative to other members of their own organization, will experience

(1) a high rate of employee turnover
(2) a high level of political activity
(3) a high rate of absenteeism
(4) complaints about the unfairness of the system

SUMMARY OF DIRECTIONS

A	B	C	D	E
1, 2, 3 only	1, 3 only	2, 4 only	4 only	All are correct

360. An employee's satisfaction with pay is affected by which of the following considerations?

(1) How the pay compares with pay received by others in the organization

(2) How the pay compares with what the employees could make elsewhere

(3) What attributes the employee brings to the job (e.g., experience, seniority)

(4) What the employee believes should count as inputs to the work

361. Individuals in an organization are apt to demonstrate which of the following characteristics?

(1) They are more influenced by their immediate surroundings than by the larger social context of the organization

(2) They are apt to give total psychological allegiance as a member of their employing organization

(3) Members occupying positions at the very top of an organization are apt to have ties to other organizations

(4) In spite of belonging to various formal groups within an organization, an individual tends to simultaneously belong to one informal social group

362. True statements about social relationships of elderly people include

(1) after age 70 less than 50 percent of women have a living husband

(2) elderly couples who are relatively distant, psychologically and geographically, from their children seem to experience greater satisfaction with life

(3) since 1960, studies have shown that twice as many old people who are ill or bedfast remain at home rather than in institutions

(4) more men than women bring their in-laws to live in their homes

363. The basic technology of native-American medicine utilizes

(1) drugs

(2) mechanical treatment

(3) religious or spiritual practices

(4) blood-letting

364. Research has established which of the following gender-related differences?

(1) Females have greater verbal ability

(2) Males have better visual-spatial skills

(3) Males excel in mathematical skills

(4) Males are more aggressive

DIRECTIONS: Each group of questions below consists of lettered headings followed by a set of numbered items. For each numbered item select the **one** lettered heading with which it is **most** closely associated. Each lettered heading may be used **once, more than once, or not at all.**

Questions 365-369

For each of the descriptions below, match the appropriate term.

(A) Authoritarian personality
(B) Discrimination
(C) Ethnic group
(D) Prejudice
(E) Minority

365. A group distinguished on the basis of socially or culturally acquired lifeways

366. An attitude of aversion or hostility toward members of another group simply because they are members and presumed to have the same objectionable characteristics attributed to the group

367. Denial of power, privilege, or status to members of one group whose qualifications are equal to those of the dominant group

368. Rigid, conventional thinking, highly judgmental values, and a cynical and "fascist" mind-set

369. A social aggregate or group that has hereditary membership and a high degree of in-group marriage and suffers oppression by a dominant segment

Questions 370-373

For each concept relating to groups, select the investigator with whom it is most closely associated.

(A) Robert K. Merton
(B) Erving Goffman
(C) Solomon Asch
(D) George Herbert Mead
(E) Dorwin Cartwright

370. The "generalized other" and development of "self"

371. An individual's "reference group"

372. A "performance team"

373. Group influence on individual perception and judgment

Sociocultural Patterns

Answers

337. The answer is D. *(Baron, ed 4. pp 534-535.)* Following World War II, many social psychologists studied the causes of fascism and anti-Semitism. Theodore Adorno and coworkers developed the F-scale (for fascism), which they believed to be a measure of the authoritarian personality. Persons scoring high on the F-scale generally are very rigid in their thinking, very aware of status differences between themselves and others, highly deferential to superiors, very strict with subordinates, and generally prejudiced toward ethnic and minority groups.

338. The answer is D. *(Lindzey, ed 3. pp 858-859.)* While fearfulness, confusion, interpersonal conflict, and regression can generate stress that can have a direct effect on biological responses, the loss of perceived control can take an even greater toll on the body. Excessive-workload and job responsibility are stressful factors in terms of coronary risk, but they become even more powerful and biologically more destructive when they approach the limit of an individual's capacity to control his or her own work. Whether the stress is from employment, unemployment, finance, family, disease, or other factors, the threat of loss or actual loss of control over one's being or activities appears to be the most devastating influence. Different individuals also have considerable variability in their responsiveness to a lack of or loss of control; this responsiveness then has a subsequent effect on their biological processes.

339. The answer is B. *(Twaddle, ed 2. pp 175-176.)* Curanderismo is a Mexican-American conception of disease that identifies imbalances of heat and cold within the body as the major cause of disease or illness. Certain diseases are considered hot and others cold. Hot foods (e.g., rice, pork, beans, onions, beer, and goat's milk) are used to cure cold illnesses (e.g., measles and ear infections), and cold foods (e.g., lamb, corn, tortillas, peas, cow's milk, and oatmeal) are used to cure hot illnesses (e.g., bleeding and skin disorders). Foods and herbs are considered hot or cold on the basis of their relationship to hot and cold forces within the body, not according to actual temperature. Curanderos practice as soloists and are respected and valued because they reflect and reinforce the culture of the barrio—the community. They share the same value system, norms, and symbol systems. The healer is truly of the people. This cultural congruence between healer and patient produces a close healer-patient relationship of the type that is all too rare in Western scientific medicine.

340. The answer is D. *(Vander Zanden, ed 4. pp 213-215.)* Most sociologists consider a norm to be a shared expectation concerning the behavior of a group or a particular person in a particular role. If a norm is violated, some type of sanction or punishment generally will be imposed on the violator. Although average behavior may be considered "normal," it is not normative unless it meets shared expectations and is subject to enforcement.

341. The answer is D. *(Steers, ed 3. pp 264-274.)* The purpose of maintaining a positive correlation between job performance and job satisfaction is to encourage good performers to remain in an organization and poor performers to leave. By paying good performers only slightly more than poor performers, an organization will maintain equal levels of satisfaction in both groups, since good performers know they are worth more and poor performers accept the fact they are worth less. Paying good performers much more than poor performers, however, keeps good performers highly satisfied and poor performers dissatisfied, which may be the desired end. Giving all employees equal raises produces the reverse effect—good performers become dissatisfied because they know they are worth more, while poor performers will be satisfied because they know they are worth less. Paying all employees what they are worth on the marketplace leads to equal levels of satisfaction among all employees, as does, of course, paying all employees more than their market value.

342. The answer is D. *(Steers, ed 3. pp 222-247.)* Some type of control system is necessary in any organization in order to determine whether the organization is meeting its goals and objectives and to evaluate its effectiveness. An organization may rely on coercion, remuneration, social pressure, or on any combination of these to control the behavior of its members. A hazard of organization control systems is their occasional tendency to produce resistance in the organization's members. For example, employees may concentrate their efforts on meeting the standards for control without contributing to the overall effectiveness of the organization. This effect of controls is called "bureaucratic" behavior. Control systems are more effective when the individuals or groups being controlled can contribute to a determination of the level at which standards are set and when such systems involve clear, objective, and flexible standards of performance.

343. The answer is A. *(Middlebrook, ed 2. pp 155-195.)* Racial prejudice is often so thoroughly learned that it is extremely difficult to modify. However, the most effective means of reducing racial prejudice has been found to be interracial contact. Since most black-white prejudices are formed in the context of lack of contact, prevention and attitude change can best be accomplished by multiple opportunities for blacks and whites to get to know each other. It is also important to recognize that the interracial situation should consist of equality of black-white status, a need for cooperation, very few members with negative stereotypes about each other, intimacy of interaction, and antiprejudice social norms and expectations. Introducing black studies into elementary school curricula, improving the black image in the mass media, legislating against prejudiced behavior, and the use of psychotherapy in treating black-white confrontation have all been of assistance in reducing prejudice, but have not proved as powerful as interracial contact.

344. The answer is B. *(Andres, pp 53-71.)* The number of persons over the age 65 years has continued to increase in this century from 3.1 million in 1900 to 24.1 million in 1978. The proportion of the over-65 age group also rose from 4.1 percent to 11 percent. By the year 2000, the over-65 age group was expected to increase to 32 million and 12 percent of the population, but present declining mortality could result in 38 million and about 14 percent of the total population by the year 2000. In 1978, the over-75 age group was 38 percent of the total over-65 age group, and it is estimated that by 2003 the over-75 age group will have increased to about 47 percent. Thus more of the population has been reaching the 65-and-older age group, and living longer, and will continue to do so. Also, among the elderly the female population has progressively outnumbered the male population. The 80 men per 100 women in the 65-to-69-year-old group decreases to 45 men per 100 women in the 85-and-over population. While the 80 men per 100 women in the 65-to-69-year-old group is expected to rise slightly to 82 by the year 2000 and 83 by 2020, the men per 100 women in the 85-and-over group is expected to fall to 39 in 2000 and slightly below 39 by 2020. In terms of institutionalization, only about 5 percent of the over-65 age group are in institutions (e.g., long-term facilities and nursing homes), which means that about 95 percent of the elderly are attempting to live with some measure of independence. A disproportional number of the institutionalized elderly are white (94 percent), and there are twice as many females as males.

345. The answer is D. *(Rosen, pp 13-15.)* Persons who tend to focus more on feelings and bodily changes have been shown to be more likely to experience disturbing and distressing states. Self-awareness achieved through such acts as being aware of test results and receiving patient education or counseling are positively correlated to psychological and physical health. Introspectiveness, however, emerges as the strongest predictor of distress, overshadowing all other predictors.

346. The answer is B. *(Twaddle, ed 2. pp 131-132.)* Studies by Zborowski (1952, 1969) revealed that American Italians and Jews were much more likely to be open and vocal about their discomfort than were Americans of Irish or "Old American" descent (the classification "Old American" refers to persons having several generations of ancestors born in the United States). The Italians focused on the pain itself, whereas the Jews worried about what the pain portended for the future. The Irish seemed to deny the existence of the pain, whereas the "Old Americans" described the pain in detail in a detached and scientific manner. Pain was measured both by an individual's subjective ratings of discomfort on a scale from 1 to 10 and by responses on a standardized questionnaire.

347. The answer is A. *(Rosen, pp 38-41.)* Scandinavian, Canadian, and American studies comparing the alcohol drinking patterns of women with those of men show that women have significantly higher morbidity and mortality as a result of alcohol consumption. For example, they are more successful with suicide, and more apt to die from both accidents and cirrhosis of the liver. The more toxic effect of alcohol on the hypothalamic-pituitary-gonadal axis in women and genetic predispositions are thought to be prominent factors. Women are known to drink less than men in general, and even less in mixed company. The overall severity of alcoholism in women is less than in men. Some of this is attributed to the fact that social norms are less tolerant of heavy drinking in women. Because of the effects of alcohol on such factors as fertility, miscarriage, cirrhosis, suicide, and sexual dysfunction, the cost to society of comparable levels of alcoholism appears to be even greater for women than men.

348. The answer is D. *(Twaddle, ed 2. p 132.)* There are no ethnic differences in **threshold** for the sensation of pain. The ethnic **response** to pain, however, is highly variable and is conditioned by cultural factors. The ethnic significance and traditions of emotionalism or stoicism regarding pain are major factors in accounting for this variable response to pain.

349. The answer is D. *(Lerner, 1984. pp 204-207.)* There has been a great increase in teen-age use of alcohol. About 80 percent of those 12 to 17 years old report having had a drink in the past; more than 50 percent report drinking once a month; more than 30 percent drink once or twice a week; and 3 percent report drinking each day. Since 1966, the number reporting that they become intoxicated at least once a month has doubled, from 10 to 20 percent. Of the male high school seniors, 80 percent report that they drink once a month, and more than 6 percent report daily drinking. Alcohol-related accidents are the leading cause of death in those 15 to 24 years old, and 60 percent of all alcohol-related highway fatalities are among young people.

350. The answer is D. *(Twaddle, ed 2. pp 179-180.)* Chinese-American medicine assumes that each person has a vital force. In each person's life force there is a conflict between yin and yang, the cold and hot forces, respectively. Many treatments are associated with restoration of the appropriate balance of yin and yang. Foods and herbals are most commonly used for this purpose.

351. The answer is B. *(Twaddle, ed 2. pp 146-147.)* Talcott Parson's formulation of society's expectations concerning the "sick role" sees that role as consisting of norms defining two rights and two obligations that are attached to persons defined as being sick. These persons have the right to be exempt from normal social activity and the right to be defined as "not responsible" for their condition. They have the obligation to define the state of being sick as undesirable, which implies that they must seek to get well and not take advantage of any secondary gains involved in being sick, such as gaining attention from others. They have the obligation to seek technically competent help and cooperate in the process of trying to get well.

352. The answer is B. *(Twaddle, ed 2. pp 172-174.)* Most spiritual healers consider disease to be a result of psychological conflicts. Stress produced by this conflict ultimately yields symptoms that are identified as a disease entity. Healers believe that the conflict and stress will be relieved once affected patients submit to the larger plan of God. Some spiritual healers explain disease as the result of original sin or the disenchantment of heavenly spirits. The parapsychological perspective speculates that there is a radical interchange of energy between body, mind, and the psychoid or Jungian collective unconscious. The healing process involves a large-scale exchange of energy and equates an emotionally charged atmosphere with energy transfer and rapid resolution of illness. Some healers recognize a germ-mechanical theory of disease where germs cause a deterioration of physical systems and recommend that patients seek resolution of the germ problem before spiritual healing can succeed. Few spiritual healers subscribe to the notion that disease results from the invasion of the body by evil spirits.

353. The answer is A. *(Brody, ed 2. pp 9-12.)* A Senate Select Committee on Nutrition and Human Needs provided a new set of nutritional guidelines for Americans. It was intended to have an influence on conditions such as heart disease, cancers of the colon and breast, stroke, high blood pressure, obesity, diabetes, arteriosclerosis, and cirrhosis of the liver, all of which are linked to the current American diet. In comparing the current diet with the proposed dietary goals, the committee recommended that proteins continue to constitute 12 percent of the diet; that total fat intake be reduced from 42 to 30 percent, with saturated fats dropping from 16 to 10 percent; that the total carbohydrate intake be raised from 46 to 58 percent, with complex carbohydrates, inculding naturally occurring sugars, increasing from 28 to 48 percent. The percentage of refined and processed sugars consumed should drop from 18 to 10 percent. Salt, alcohol, and cholesterol consumption should all be reduced, whereas the intake of roughage should be increased.

354. The answer is E (all). *(Andres, pp 957-958.)* Patients facing the threat of death most often exhibit physical and emotional reactions to loss. The most frequent losses are of independence, self-image, control, and financial security. The loss of independence is particularly upsetting to persons who have always taken care of their own physical needs but who now need help with simple daily tasks. The dependency generated by intense pain is of great concern to dying patients. Earning power, mobility, and family or job role are also important parts of independence. Loss of self-image through change of personal appearance, weakness, disfigurement, and embarrassing altered body function is also disturbing. Loss of control is one of the most upsetting conflicts and often results from the control and authority assumed by the medical profession. Patients often fear that they will be abandoned if they do not relinquish complete control over their lives. The loss of financial resources engendered by illness, e.g., the threat of financial hardship or loss of one's entire life savings, is also of major concern for the dying patient.

355. The answer is E (all). *(Rosen, pp 97-98.)* Dieting induced by social and cultural pressures initiates a process of biological cognitive and behavioral dis-regulation. The first effect of reducing the intake of calories is a lowered basal metabolic rate, which does not immediately increase after the dieting has ceased; this results in a net increase in calories and weight. Also, hormonal changes occur after dieting, especially after severe dieting, that actually promote fat storage. Other biological changes induced by dieting include plateaus in weight loss, cravings, or binges, and the frequent development of increasingly compulsive strategies in at-tempts to lose weight. These mechanisms can actually result in weight gain.

356. The answer is A (1, 2, 3). *(Steptoe, pp 201-203.)* Physicians must consider the values held and conditions experienced by patients if they expect the patient to comply with recommended actions. In general, the more complex the recommended actions, the longer the duration of time required for the treatment, and the more the patient sees the treatment as interfering with his or her own personal behavior, the less complete compliance one can expect. Compliance is most often related to such factors as threat to health, disabling symptoms, social support, personal and contin-uous source of care, cooperative relationship with health professionals, and a knowl-edge of the nature and rationale for the specific treatment recommendations. The cost paid for treatment is more apt to be positively than negatively related to compliance.

357. The answer is E (all). *(Middlebrook, ed 2. pp 322-349.)* Many people avoid taking action in an emergency situation. The farther away the bystander is and the more people present, the less likely is a bystander to get involved. One is more apt to help the more one knows what to do, the fewer people present, if one is a male, if the victim does not appear to be responsible for his or her mishap (e.g., stroke victim vs. drunk), if the negative consequences to the bystander are minimal and the positive consequences reasonable, if the bystander's freedom is not limited by helping, if the bystander is somehow forced to get involved, if someone else is acting as a helping model, and if the victim is dependent or without resources, or has helped the bystander in the past. Altruism is most easily learned through positive reinforcement and imitation.

358. The answer is A (1, 2, 3). *(Atchley, pp 241-243.)* As individuals age or retire they can replace their old roles with new roles and activities, concentrate and redirect their energies on the roles and activities that remain, or they can withdraw. Consolidation of commitments and redistribution of one's energy is the most frequent mechanism of coping with lost roles, activities, or capacities. This usually involves redistributing time and energies among remaining roles and activities. Problems arise, however, with individuals who have so few roles or activities that there are not enough to absorb the energies freed by the loss. Substitution of new roles and activities is an obvious alternative; however, substitute roles are not always available, especially if there is income decline, physical decline, or little motivation to find a meaningful substitute. Disengagement is a withdrawal from roles or activities, and a reduction of activity level or sense of involvement. Disengagement is not inevitable and depends on opportunities, interests, and motivation. A form of differential disengagement, similar to consolidation, is more apt to occur. The degree of disengagement also appears to be related to the degree of perceived threat to the living conditions of the elderly and the attitudes of others toward the elderly. The balance between consolidation, substitution, and disengagement is very dependent on good health. Poor health is more apt to force an individual into disengagement. Disorganization is maladaptive and infrequent.

359. The answer is C (2, 4). *(Steers, ed 3. pp 276-287.)* Employees who are paid well relative to their counterparts in other organizations are likely to stay in their jobs and have a high attendance. However, if they feel they are underpaid relative to fellow workers in their own organization, such individuals will feel that they are being treated unfairly. This dissatisfaction will generate complaints and a high level of political activity.

360. The answer is E (all). *(Steers, ed 3. pp 231-247.)* According to J. Stacy Adams's equity theory, employees' satisfaction with pay is determined by the ratio of their outcomes to their inputs for the job and how that ratio compares with the ratios of others, both in the organization and outside it. Different employees may include different factors as inputs; thus, hours worked, quality of work, education, seniority, and other factors may be considered as inputs by some and not by others.

361. The answer is B (1, 3). *(Steers, ed 3. pp 386-399, 425-439.)* Individuals and groups of individuals are the units that make up organizations. Organizations are distinguished from simple collections of individuals by having goals and objectives. The individuals who belong to an organization generally are influenced more by their immediate surroundings than by the larger social context; therefore, members are more likely to be responsive to their immediate work group, for example, than to the organization of which it is a part. Because every individual belongs to several groups and organizations (e.g., family, religious groups), no single group or organization can command one's total psychological allegiance. Even individuals who occupy positions at the very top of their organizations, those who have the most to gain or lose in relation to the organization's fate, have ties to other social entities or organizations that they could not eliminate entirely, even if they wanted to do so.

An individual usually belongs to several formal groups within an organization, but also simultaneously belongs to several informal social groups within the organization.

362. The answer is A (1, 2, 3). *(Ebersole, ed 2. pp 498-508.)* Even though the most significant and binding relationship in old age is usually that of the couple, there is little likelihood of a couple's going through old age together. After age 70, less than 50 percent of women have a living husband. While families are important to the elderly to promote a sense of belonging, aged couples who are relatively distant, psychologically and geographically, from their children seem to fare the best. Apparently, they do not expect their children to meet their needs, nor are they required to meet their children's needs. Thus, the relationships between children and elderly couples appear to be of less significance than was previously thought. The most relevant factor appears to be the quality of close relationships, rather than the frequency of contact. Illness is another factor that concerns old people and their families; however, instead of resorting to institutional confinement when they are ill or bedfast, statistics indicate that twice as many old people who are ill or bedfast remain at home rather than resort to institutions, as was the case in 1960. More women than men will bring in-laws to live in their homes. However, help given to a parent-in-law tends to be more ritualized, with preference for phone contacts rather than face-to-face contact.

363. The answer is A (1, 2, 3). *(Twaddle, ed 2. p 178.)* In contrast to Western scientific medicine, practitioners of native-American medicine never considered bloodletting to be of medical value. They have employed a wide variety of drugs, however, such as astringents, emetics, sedatives, stimulants, antibiotics, and even pharmacological contraceptives. Mechanical treatments have included quarantine, sweat baths, bathing in mineral springs, surgery, and immobilization of broken limbs. Spiritual methods employed in native-American medicine and carried out by a shaman include group singing, incantations, and facilitation of communication with the spirits by smoking the peace pipe.

364. The answer is E (all). *(Schuster, ed 2. p 321.)* Many misconceptions have developed regarding gender-related differences, often to justify role stereotyping. In actuality, only four gender-related differences have been established through empirical research in the United States. The differences that have been found consistently are as follows: females have greater verbal ability, males have better visual-spatial skills, males excel in mathematical skills, and males are more aggressive.

365-369. The answers are: 365-C, 366-D, 367-B, 368-A, 369-E. *(Vander Zanden, ed 4. pp 409, 460-465, 467-471, 490.)* An ethnic group is a group distinguished on the basis of socially acquired lifeways. The members are usually biologically related and are related on the basis of common customs or culture (e.g., Italian or Irish).

Prejudice is described as a hostile or aversive attitude toward the members of a group simply because they belong to it and are therefore presumed to have the same objectionable qualities attributed to the group. The basic factors that characterize prejudice in the dominant group are feelings of superiority; the perception that the minority group is inherently different and alien; a claim to power, privilege, or status; and a fear or suspicion that the minority group wants the power, privilege, or status of the dominant group. Also, prejudice has a cognitive component (mental image), an affective component (feelings or emotions), and a behavioral component (predisposition to act).

Discrimination is an arbitrary denial of power, privilege, or status to a group (usually a minority) whose qualifications are equal to those of the dominant group. It is important to note that prejudice may or may not be associated with discrimination.

The authoritarian personality is characterized by rigid and conventional thinking, obsession with power and submission to authority, and highly judgmental values. T. W. Adorno characterized the authoritarian personality as having a mind-set similar to that of a fascist. There does appear to be a link between prejudice and authoritarianism.

A minority group is any racial or ethnic group that has hereditary membership, a consciousness of oneness, and a high degree of in-group marriage and usually suffers oppression from a dominant (majority) segment of a nation or state. The members often find themselves disadvantaged in terms of privilege and status, and the minority is often the source of the dominant group's advantages.

370-373. The answers are: 370-D, 371-A, 372-B, 373-C. *(Vander Zanden, ed 4. pp 147-151, 220-223, 256, 418-422.)* George Herbert Mead put forth a theory of the development of the "self," a development that he viewed as possible because language allows humans to treat themselves as objects, seeing themselves through the eyes of others. He argued that through play and other organized social activity a child takes on various roles and learns the attitudes of the others involved. To participate effectively in social activity, a child must comprehend the complicated role relationships that exist among the participants. Through such exposure, children gradually learn the generalized norms and attitudes of their social group or community, which Mead termed the "generalized other."

The work of Robert K. Merton and Harold Kelley argues strongly for the significance of reference groups in determining a person's social experience. Two kinds of reference groups are distinguished: normative reference groups, from which a person derives the values and norms that influence that person's behavior, and comparative reference groups, against which persons evaluate their individual performance. The question arises as to what motivates a person to choose a particular reference group, either a membership group to which that person belongs, or a nonmembership group to which that person might aspire to belong. Merton has suggested that the more able a nonmembership group is to confer status on a person, and the more socially isolated that person is within a membership group, the more likely such an individual will choose a nonmembership reference group for purposes of comparison.

In arriving at the concept of a performance team, Erving Goffman observes that a group of individuals frequently must cooperate in a performance. The front so presented is a joint production; any team member has the power to "give away" the performance by breaking character and violating the shared definition of the situation held by the team members. However, teammates who are cooperating in a routine also have "off camera" relationships among themselves, so that a distinction can be made between the behavior exhibited "on stage" (e.g., before the diners in a restaurant) and "backstage" (e.g., in the kitchen where the diners are not permitted).

Solomon Asch conducted a series of experiments and found that individuals in a group will actually change their perceptions (such as estimating the length of a line), their judgments (yielding to the majority and reporting not what they saw but what they felt must be correct), and their actions (yielding so as not to appear different or stupid in the eyes of other group members). In the distortion of perception the individual incorporates within his or her personality the standards of behavior that are prevalent in the group. Distortion of action illustrates the distinction between private acceptance (attitude change) and compliance (without private acceptance). Patients in medicine often yield to the same influences of physicians or other patients when they report their history or reactions to therapy.

Human Ecology
and Health

DIRECTIONS: Each question below contains five suggested responses. Select the **one best** response to each question.

374. Obesity has been well documented as a primary contributing factor in the development of each of the following diseases EXCEPT

(A) adult-onset diabetes
(B) hypertension
(C) gallbladder disease
(D) arthritis
(E) myocardial hypertrophy

375. Yearly studies of drug use by high school seniors have reported all the following EXCEPT that

(A) between 1975 and 1981 the almost daily use of marijuana decreased from 11 percent to 7 percent
(B) between 1979 and 1981 there was an increase in seniors labeling marijuana as a ''great risk'' from 35 percent to 58 percent
(C) most illicit drug use has been declining since the peak of the 1970s
(D) between 1976 and 1979 cocaine use rose sharply from 6 to 12 percent
(E) amphetamines have decreased in use, so that in 1981 only 10 percent have tried them without medical supervision

376. All the following statements about teenage smoking are true EXCEPT that

(A) the age for beginning smoking is decreasing
(B) the majority of female smokers begin smoking after they are 13 years of age
(C) 12 percent of those 12 to 17 years of age smoke
(D) 26 percent of those 17 to 18 years of age smoke
(E) one-third of all 18-year-olds are regular smokers

377. Which of the following social variables is most closely linked to infant mortality?

(A) Poverty
(B) Education of mother
(C) Education of father
(D) Occupation of father
(E) Marital status of parents

378. In studies of hundreds of records of cancer patients, the most frequently noted problem for patients posthospitalization is

(A) anxiety
(B) pain
(C) impairment of family relationships
(D) suicidal thoughts
(E) depression

379. Each of the following statements about minorities and the use of alcohol and the incidence of alcohol problems is true EXCEPT (*Some for* $\varphi \propto \varphi$ *20 – 32%*)

(A) Asian Americans tend to drink less than non-Asian Americans
(B) rates of alcoholism among Hispanic Americans tend to be higher than the national average
(C) when American Indians enter an urban environment, the rate of alcoholism becomes much worse
(D) alcoholism among blacks appears to be increasing
(E) the incidence of alcoholism among homosexuals appears to be greater among females

380. Each of the following statements about sleep problems is true EXCEPT that *20% insomnia*

(A) the number of people who have a sleep problem is about 50 percent
(B) pain and trouble sleeping are the two most common complaints in medicine
(C) insomnia is the chronic inability to obtain the necessary amount or quality of sleep to maintain adequate daytime behavior
(D) there is little evidence that sleeping medication is effective for more than several days
(E) there is an excessive tendency for poor sleepers to self-medicate and for physicians to over-prescribe strong sleeping pills

381. What percentage of the mortality from the 10 leading causes of death in the United States can be traced to lifestyle?

(A) 10
(B) 20
(C) 30
(D) 40
(E) 50

382. Most of the major health problems of adolescents

(A) have a genetic basis
(B) have a sexual basis
(C) involve sensory deficits
(D) are self-inflicted
(E) involve bacterial and viral infections

383. The greatest potential for health promotion will result from all the following EXCEPT

(A) changing the typical stance of dependence in the relationship with professionals
(B) development of more healthful patterns of daily living
(C) risk factor intervention
(D) more effective adaptation to the presence of chronic illness
(E) increased utilization of physician services

384. Which of the following causes a person to use the most calories per hour above basal metabolism?

(A) Bicycling (moderate speed)
(B) Walking (3 mph)
(C) Dancing (fox-trot)
(D) Swimming (2 mph)
(E) Horseback riding (trot)

385. Nutritional experts have recommended all the following tips for weight control EXCEPT

(A) eating slowly
(B) taking small portions of food
(C) waiting 20 minutes before taking a second helping
(D) watching television or reading while you are eating
(E) recording all food intake in a "dietary diary"

386. The following statements about alcohol and alcoholism are true EXCEPT that

(A) 10 percent of men and 3 to 5 percent of women develop alcoholism
(B) the homeless or skid-row alcoholic represents over 25 percent of all alcoholics
(C) there is considerable genetic variability controlling an individual's response to alcohol
(D) 10 g of ethanol is equal to about 12 oz of beer, 4 oz of nonfortified wine, and 1.5 oz of 80-proof beverage
(E) alcoholics have a carcinoma rate 10 times higher than that of the general population

387. Empirical findings about patterns of disease and illness include all the following EXCEPT

(A) a large range of symptoms, e.g., headache, upset stomach, and sore muscles, is found in the general population on any given day
(B) a very small percentage of persons experiencing symptoms of disease or illness seeks medical care
(C) individual persons show highly diverse reactions to the presence of many disease symptoms
(D) it is important for physicians to understand how patients interpret their perceived physical signs and symptoms
(E) persons are relatively independent of communication from others in deciding on the meaning of their own unexpected physiological changes

[handwritten notes in top margin: Thyroxin needed for normal brain development]

388. All the following statements about hyperthyroidism are true EXCEPT that it *[handwritten: hypothyroidine causes mental retardation]*

(A) may be the cause of a frank psychosis

(B) is more frequent in women than in men

(C) may be precipitated by acute emotional stress

(D) is associated with mental retardation in children

(E) is associated with tension and hyperexcitability

389. All the following statements about obesity are true EXCEPT that

(A) obesity increases the risk of developing diabetes approximately fourfold

(B) obese persons are more likely to die in automobile accidents than are members of the population in general

(C) obesity increases the severity of most health problems

(D) obesity is the leading cause of hypertension

(E) obesity has been linked to complications from surgery and infections

390. Adolescents represent about 17 percent of the population (40 million citizens) yet they account for all the following EXCEPT

(A) over twice as many automobile accidents as adults

(B) 20 percent of all suicides (5,000 to 7,000 adolescent suicides per year)

(C) over 600,000 pregnancies in unmarried girls per year

(D) the only age group for which the death rate is actually decreasing

(E) an age group of which about 12 percent smoke

391. The major cause of death among adolescents and young adults is

(A) homicide

(B) suicide

(C) motor vehicle accidents

(D) infections

(E) illicit drug abuse

392. All the following are highly ranked health problems and concerns as expressed by adolescents EXCEPT

(A) colds   *[handwritten: most 70%]*

(B) depression   *[handwritten: 48%]*

(C) venereal disease

(D) personal problems   *[handwritten: 42%]*

(E) acne   *[handwritten: 34%]*

DIRECTIONS: Each question below contains four suggested responses of which **one or more** is correct. Select

A	if	**1, 2, and 3**	are correct
B	if	**1 and 3**	are correct
C	if	**2 and 4**	are correct
D	if	**4**	is correct
E	if	**1, 2, 3, and 4**	are correct

393. Among college students, heavy alcohol drinkers

(1) tend to come from large metropolitan rather than rural areas
(2) are more likely to major in the natural than the social sciences
(3) tend not to be deeply religious
(4) use nonalcoholic drugs less frequently than nondrinkers

394. An adolescent has an increased risk of becoming a smoker if he or she has

(1) employment outside the home
(2) parents who smoke
(3) friends who smoke
(4) adult role models who smoke

395. Fordyce's classical behavioral approach to pain is based on which of the following concepts?

(1) Behavior in response to pain is significant in its own right
(2) Environmental consequences have a strong effect on pain-related behavior
(3) Behavior is observable and measurable
(4) Understanding internal causative factors of conflict or anxiety is crucial

396. Environmental influences on pain and pain-related behavior involve which of the following learning mechanisms?

(1) Operant conditioning
(2) Classical conditioning
(3) Observational learning
(4) Latent learning

397. Known predictors of morbidity and longevity include which of the following factors?

(1) Income level
(2) Education level
(3) Marital status
(4) Religious participation

398. Correct statements about insomnia include which of the following?

(1) The most common causes of insomnia are psychological and emotional disturbances
(2) Anxiety is positively correlated with difficulty in falling asleep
(3) Depression is positively correlated with frequency of early awakenings
(4) The most frequent emotional cause of insomnia is anxiety

399. During the first year of mourning and bereavement, an individual has increased vulnerability to which of the following diseases?

(1) Cancer
(2) Rheumatic disease
(3) Heart disease
(4) Kidney disease

400. Use of drugs by the elderly can be characterized by which of the following statements?

(1) Over-the-counter medications account for 40 percent of drugs consumed
(2) Psychotropic agents surpass all other drugs consumed by the institutionalized elderly
(3) Over half of patients over age 60 make one or more medication errors during each illness
(4) A high risk factor for adverse drug reactions is being a male

401. Predictors of morbidity and longevity include which of the following markers?

(1) Gender
(2) Income
(3) Age
(4) Marital status

402. Accurate statements regarding our knowledge of intervention and skills in changing health behavior include which of the following?

(1) We do not know much about how to help people change initially, but are reasonably successful at helping them sustain the new behavior
(2) We are not well informed about preparing and motivating people to undertake change
(3) We know more about health promotion than about risk reduction
(4) We know very little about how people successfully change their own behavior

403. Behavioral research on nutrition and obesity has demonstrated that

(1) eating is often a response to, compensation for, or defense against tension and frustration
(2) analyzing conditions under which one usually eats facilitates weight control
(3) psychological makeup of the individual influences eating behaviors and activity levels
(4) there are identifiable personality factors common to persons who have difficulty making a satisfactory weight adjustment

SUMMARY OF DIRECTIONS

A	B	C	D	E
1, 2, 3 only	1, 3 only	2, 4 only	4 only	All are correct

404. True statements regarding health beliefs include which of the following?

- (1) The majority of individuals with hypertension believe they can monitor their own blood pressure with signs and symptoms
- (2) Patients assign more validity to their physician's instructions than to their self-assessment of their health
- (3) Patients who believe they can control their health outcome are more apt to change their health-related behavior
- (4) Younger patients are more apt to believe that controlling their emotions and staying mentally active are important preventive actions

405. Research findings on the use of alcoholic beverages show which of the following?

- (1) The alcoholic's life span is shortened by 10 to 12 years
- (2) Alcohol is considered to be a contributory cause in half of all deaths resulting from automobile accidents
- (3) Current use rates of alcohol are higher for young adults (18–25 years of age) than for older adults (26+ years of age)
- (4) Behavioral treatment of problem drinking and alcoholism has shown that total, complete, and permanent abstinence is considered a necessary treatment objective

406. Psychosocial stimuli beneficial in the treatment of childhood or adult asthma include

- (1) systematic desensitization
- (2) family therapy
- (3) implosion
- (4) relaxation training

407. Life-style refers to those individual and societal behavior patterns that are at least partly under individual control and that demonstrably influence personal health. Health status and life-style behaviors are linked because

(1) the major causes of death, serious illness, and disability in the United States today are chronic disease and violence
(2) behind most chronic disease, disability, and premature death are many life-style factors that are potentially amenable to change
(3) a few life-style patterns (e.g., smoking, drinking alcohol) constitute the major behavioral risk factors involved in chronic disease and severe disability
(4) educational techniques that modify life-style patterns can improve both preventive and curative medical practices

408. In the U.S. in 1980, homicide

(1) was frequently (45 percent of the time) committed by individuals known to their victims
(2) was the leading cause of death for black or minority young people (15 to 34 years old)
(3) ranked eleventh among all causes of death
(4) was most frequently committed with a blunt instrument or knife

409. Patients with metastatic breast cancer live significantly longer if they are

(1) negatively reactive
(2) married
(3) hostile
(4) passive and cooperative

410. Behavioral prodromes of myocardial infarction and sudden death include

(1) emotional exhaustion
(2) feelings of despair
(3) hopelessness
(4) depression

411. Research studies support which of the following findings about the health consequences of smoking behavior?

(1) Approximately 18 percent of all mortality in the United States is smoking-related
(2) Most deaths caused by bronchitis/emphysema are smoking-related
(3) Most deaths caused by lung cancer are smoking-related
(4) Most deaths caused by cancer of the oral cavity are smoking-related

412. True statements about smoking include that

(1) the most effective deterrent to substance abuse is fear arousal
(2) the major influence on teenagers to smoke comes from their peers
(3) the social context is the excuse, but not the reason for maintaining a smoking habit
(4) the most rapid increase in smoking is among teenage females

		SUMMARY OF DIRECTIONS		
A	B	C	D	E
1, 2, 3 only	1, 3 only	2, 4 only	4 only	All are correct

413. Studies of birth weight of human infants show that

(1) black mothers give birth to small babies (2,500 g or less) at a higher rate than do white mothers
(2) the most significant characteristic associated with a poor pregnancy outcome is low birth weight
(3) low birth weight babies, when compared with heavier babies, are likely to have a greater rate of developmental problems (epilepsy, cerebral palsy, mental retardation)
(4) the most frequently cited factors contributing to low birth weight are poor nutrition, smoking, stress, and poor physical condition

414. Statistics on adolescent suicide show which of the following patterns?

(1) Boys are three times more likely to commit suicide than are girls
(2) Adolescents between the ages of 15 and 19 years old accounted for 6.6 percent of the 25,000 suicides committed in the United States in 1976
(3) Between 1950 and 1975, the suicide rate for teenage boys increased
(4) Boys tend to choose more violent methods for committing suicide than do girls

415. True statements about the health consequences of smoking include that

(1) the overall mortality risk is 60 percent greater for smokers than for nonsmokers
(2) the risk of dying of lung cancer is between 8 and 15 times higher in a cigarette smoker than in a nonsmoker
(3) life span is shortened by about 5.5 minutes for each cigarette smoked
(4) children whose parents smoke have a higher incidence of respiratory infections and impaired function than those whose parents do not smoke

416. True statements about alcohol abuse include that

(1) the percentage of families with problem-drinking men increases with age of head of household
(2) alcoholism is the second most frequent form of drug dependence after tobacco use in the United States
(3) the percentage of families with problem-drinking men (age 21–29) is approximately 5 percent—1.3 million families
(4) annual cost to industry and the economy of alcohol abuse is currently estimated to be greater than cost of tobacco-related disease and death

417. In a clinical setting, the diagnosis of alcoholism is made when an individual

(1) ignores early warning signs that alcohol is causing problems in marriage and moves ahead to separation or divorce
(2) is fired or laid-off as a result of alcohol-related problems
(3) is arrested two or more times for an alcohol offense
(4) demonstrates signs of alcoholic withdrawal

418. Women who are moderate or heavy drinkers are more apt to bear children with which of the following problems?

(1) Mental retardation
(2) Reduced growth
(3) Motor retardation
(4) Central nervous system damage

419. Patients who are ill tend to use denial when

(1) they view their social roles or personal desires to be threatened
(2) they have detected symptoms that they fear to be potentially serious and life-threatening
(3) their fears are not matched by their capacities to take meaningful action
(4) there is increased opportunity for secondary gain

420. The antidepressant effects of exercise have been linked with

(1) increased cerebral blood flow
(2) increased levels of epinephrine and norepinephrine
(3) sense of mastery and self-control
(4) cathartic inhibition

421. Exercise has been demonstrated to aid in the prevention of

(1) arthritis
(2) abnormal body weight and composition
(3) type I diabetes
(4) coronary heart disease

422. True statements regarding exercise of moderate intensity include which of the following?

(1) Thirty minutes of exercise will generally result in an energy expenditure of 300 kcal
(2) The metabolic rate remains elevated for several hours after exercise
(3) Exercise helps to retain lean body mass in the elderly
(4) When exercise is combined with calorie restriction, a greater weight loss of fat tissue is accomplished

423. Behavioral factors appear to be crucial to which of the following aspects of cigarette smoking?

(1) Initiation of the smoking habit
(2) Maintaining abstinence
(3) Day-to-day fluctuations in smoking
(4) Nicotine addiction
Pharmacological factor

424. The importance of psychosocial factors in the etiology of schizophrenia is illustrated by the fact that

(1) lower socioeconomic status correlates with a higher incidence of schizophrenia
(2) family psychosocial factors are about equal to biologic factors
(3) the stress-diathesis model has linked biological vulnerability with induction of stress
(4) there is a schizophrenia-prone personality type

425. During the first year after myocardial infarction, the majority of patients exhibit which of the following responses?

(1) Extensive disturbances in subjective state
(2) Moderate physical distress
(3) Perception of selves as handicapped
(4) Depression and anxiety

DIRECTIONS: Each group of questions below consists of lettered headings followed by a set of numbered items. For each numbered item select the **one** lettered heading with which it is **most** closely associated. Each lettered heading may be used **once, more than once, or not at all.**

Questions 426-429

For each condition, select the factor with which it is most significantly associated in the United States.

(A) Poverty
(B) Aging
(C) Heredity
(D) Religion
(E) Race

E 426. Sickle cell anemia

C 427. Phenylketonuria

B 428. Osteoarthritis

A 429. Dental decay

Questions 430-433

For each description relating to community health, choose the factor with which it is most closely associated in the United States.

(A) Income
(B) Economic and social class structure
(C) Age
(D) Religious beliefs
(E) Health beliefs

B 430. The nature and distribution of health care services

A 431. The overall health status of community members

C 432. The widest gap between need and provision of health care services

E 433. The perception of patterns of disease and their relative importance

DIRECTIONS: The group of questions below consists of four lettered headings followed by a set of numbered items. For each numbered item select

A	if the item is associated with	(A) **only**
B	if the item is associated with	(B) **only**
C	if the item is associated with	**both** (A) and (B)
D	if the item is associated with	**neither** (A) nor (B)

Each lettered heading may be used **once, more than once, or not at all.**

Questions 434-439

(A) Unipolar depression
(B) Bipolar (manic depressive) disorder
(C) Both
(D) Neither

434. Women are affected two or three times more than men

435. Average age of onset is about 30 years

436. There is recurrence about four times during the next 20 years

437. Disturbances of mood, energy, appetite, sleep, and sexual function are seen

438. A detectable psychosocial precipitant usually exists

439. A spectrum of depressive illness is involved

Human Ecology and Health

Answers

374. The answer is C. *(Rosen, pp 72-73.)* Obesity increases risks for both physical and psychological disorders. It has been well documented as a primary contributing factor in the development of adult-onset diabetes, hypertension, myocardial hypertrophy, arthritis, gout, menstrual abnormalities, and reproductive problems. It is also a secondary contributing factor in endometrial cancer. It is related to gallbladder disease and atherosclerosis, but primarily on a correlational basis.

375. The answer is E. *(Lerner, 1984. pp 153-157.)* Between 1975 and 1981, the use of marijuana by high school seniors fell from 11 percent to 7 percent (this does not include those who had dropped out of school and who often have higher rates of use). At the same time, the seniors who linked ''great risk'' to smoking marijuana regularly increased from 35 percent to 58 percent. Seventy-five percent now report that their close friends would disapprove of its regular use. In general, the use of most illicit drugs has been declining from the peak levels of the 1970s. Between 1976 and 1979, cocaine use rose from 6 to 12 percent and remains fairly steady with some regional differences (e.g., use appears to be rising in the West and Northeast). Also increasing is the use of amphetamines, with one-third of the 1981 seniors having tried them without medical supervision.

376. The answer is B. *(Lerner, 1984. pp 200-202.)* Twelve percent of teenagers 12 to 17 years old smoke, which increases to 26 percent for those 17 to 18 years old. About one-third of all 18-year-olds are regular smokers. While the teenage smoking rates appear to be decreasing, it may be that only the older group has leveled off. It is important to recognize that the age for beginning smoking is decreasing, especially for females. Sixty percent of the female smokers begin smoking before they are 13 years of age.

377. The answer is A. *(Bell, ed 6. pp 397-398.)* Poverty, the most important social variable in infant mortality, is linked to an almost 50 percent greater risk of both neonatal and postnatal death. Other social variables—such as the educational level, occupation, or income of either the mother or father, or whether the parents are married—can influence the risk of infant mortality, but none is as powerful as poverty. Poverty is also a major contributor to adult morbidity and mortality.

378. The answer is B. *(Rosen, p 288.)* Pain is the most frequently noted problem in cancer patients posthospitalization. Mood disturbances such as anxiety, depression, suicidal thoughts, and guilt are second in frequency, with the impairment of family relationships as third. Richard Lazarus has asserted that the actual number of patients struggling with general distress may be far higher, especially given the tendency of the medical profession and hospital personnel to inhibit such expression. With the current earlier discharge of hospitalized patients, these patient problems are expected to increase.

379. The answer is E. *(Rosen, pp 46-49.)* Alcoholism among both male and female homosexuals is estimated to be between 20 and 32 percent. Although there is considerable variation among races and nationalities, Asian Americans tend to drink less alcohol than non-Asian Americans. They also metabolize ethanol more quickly. Rates of alcoholism among Hispanic Americans appear to be higher than the national average and are thought to be related to sociocultural norms and values. Alcoholism among American Indians and native Alaskans is high, and the rate of alcoholism becomes even higher when American Indians from reservations enter the urban environment. Alcoholism among blacks appears to be increasing with little recognition of its threat. In terms of prevention, all minority groups suffer from a lack of targeted treatment and prevention programs; they also tend not to use the few existing programs.

380. The answer is A. *(Kandel, ed 2. pp 659-660.)* The inability to sleep is a hardship that can alter a person's mood and behavior and even disrupt a life by affecting the entire behavioral repertoire of an individual. Quantitative surveys have established that about one in five individuals has a sleep problem. Physicians report that the two most common complaints in medicine are pain and trouble sleeping. Insomnia is defined as the chronic inability to obtain the necessary amount or quality of sleep to maintain adequate daytime behavior. In reality it is a symptom of a variety of disorders. It is such a public health problem that there is an excessive tendency of poor sleepers to medicate themselves and for physicians to over-prescribe strong sleeping pills. The net result is a serious problem of abuse of sleeping medications. Various studies have shown that there is very little evidence that any current sleeping medication is effective for more than several days. A part of the reason for so much over-treatment of sleep complaints is that they are often exaggerated by patients.

381. The answer is E. *(Hamburg, pp 35-51.)* "Lifestyle" is a term used to refer to single and collective aspects of individual behavior, especially long-term patterns of behavior that characterize an individual's general habits of living, adapting, coping, and achieving. The United States Department of Health and Human Services has estimated that 50 percent of the mortality from the 10 leading causes of death can be traced to one's lifestyle. The behaviors that make up the lifestyle are the major risk factors of disease in that those individuals who engage in certain behaviors are more likely to develop certain illnesses than are those individuals who do not. Major known behavioral risk factors are cigarette smoking, certain dietary habits, reckless driving, violence, use of illicit drugs, excessive consumption of alcoholic beverages, insufficient exercise, nonadherence to medication regimens, maladaptive responses to social pressures and stress, and obesity.

382. The answer is D. *(Hamburg, pp 247-256.)* Although most American adolescents judge their own health to be very good, many adolescents take actions that produce self-induced health problems resulting in physical or behavioral disability or death. Most of these have to do with behaviors associated with accidents, drug and alcohol abuse, tobacco use, and poor eating habits. Accidents are the leading cause of death in the adolescent years, and their incidence appears to be increasing at a rapid rate. Homicide is the second leading cause of death, and suicide is the third. Drug, alcohol, and tobacco use usually begin during adolescence or even during preadolescence. Since these activities are all behaviorally related, there is at least the potential that behavioral intervention can make the greatest impact on the health of youth.

383. The answer is E. *(Last, ed 12. pp 1092-1097.)* Research studies of illness behavior and relationships with medical professionals clearly show the need for increased competency of the patient in adapting to and coping with conditions of illness and injury. This runs counter to the frequent appearance of dependency of the patient on the physician to manage and prevent an illness. Thus, the largest potential for promoting health will result from social action directed to the development of more healthful patterns of living, rather than increased utilization of physician services. Risk factor intervention and attempts to modify patterns of behavior are important strategies for improving the health status of specific population groups.

384. The answer is D. *(Guthrie, ed 6. pp 146-149.)* The calories required for physical activity above the needs of basal metabolism depend on the type of activity, the duration of activity, and the size of the person performing it. Some tables show energy expenditures based on the type of activity irrespective of the size of the individual, but allowing for body weight and intensity of the activity is more accurate. In spite of these limitations, tables of energy costs can be useful tools in nutrition and medicine. The energy cost of walking 3 miles per hour is only 2 kcal/ kg of body weight above maintenance requirements. Thus, a 60-kg (132-lb) person will burn up 120 calories and a 75-kg (165-lb) person will expend 150 calories. An hour of moderate bicycling will expend about 2.5 kcal/kg (150 calories for the 60-kg person or 190 calories for the 75-kg person). Moderately heavy activity, such as swimming (2 mph), expends 7.9 kcal/kg/hr or 474 calories per hour for the 60-kg person and 593 calories for the 75-kg person. Fox-trot dancing will expend 3.8 kcal/kg/hr, or 228 calories for the 60-kg person and 285 calories for the 75-kg person. Running will consume 7.0 kcal/kg/hr (420 or 525 calories, respectively), while rowing in a race will consume 16.0 kcal/kg/hr (960 or 1200 calories/hr).

385. The answer is D. *(Brody, ed 2. pp 312-314.)* Empirical studies have revealed a number of changes in eating habits that will significantly discourage the tendency to eat more food than is required by the body. Nutritional experts recommend that we eat more slowly, serve ourselves smaller portions, wait at least 20 minutes after we have eaten our first serving before taking a second serving, restrict all our eating to one or two places in the home, do not watch television or read while we are eating, let family and friends know that we are trying to cut down on food intake, go grocery shopping after we have eaten a satisfying meal, do not leave food out where we repeatedly see it and can easily reach it many times a day, try to spend less time in the kitchen, get someone else in the family to clear the plates and put away the leftovers, and keep a detailed log or diary of all food intake. Such activities will help to disrupt previously learned, but inappropriate, eating behaviors and establish appropriate environmental conditions and eating behaviors.

386. The answer is B. *(Braunwald, ed 11. pp 2106-2111.)* It is estimated that 90 percent of people in the U.S. drink alcohol at some time, 40 to 50 percent of men have temporary alcohol-induced problems, and 10 percent of men and 3 to 5 percent of women develop alcoholism. Even light drinking can adversely interact with other medications, heavier drinking can exacerbate most medical illnesses, and alcoholism can masquerade as other medical disorders and psychiatric syndromes. While most information on alcohol applies to the "average" person, there is considerable variability between individuals depending on genetic factors, other drug use, and existing pathology or disease. It is also little appreciated that the cancer rate with alcoholism is 10 times higher than that in the general population, especially in the head and neck, esophagus, stomach, liver, and pancreas. The homeless or skid-row alcoholic represents only 5 percent or less of all alcoholics. In general, 12 oz of beer, 4 oz of nonfortified wine, and 1.5 oz of 80-proof beverage contain the same amount (10 g) of ethanol.

387. The answer is E. *(Counte, pp 15-19.)* Symptoms of physical illness that might be defined simply as perceived or subjective changes of one's bodily state play a key role in health care. Such perceived changes, combined with observable signs, are the only way that the presence of illness can be detected. An understanding of how these symptoms and signs are interpreted by the average person is important for the practicing physician. The traditional view concerning the frequency of symptoms states that the illness experience constitutes a relatively infrequent or unusual event. In recent years, however, there have been a number of studies of symptom prevalence in normal populations; this evidence shows that there is a sizable number of clinically serious problems reported in supposedly healthy populations. Various empirical studies have reported that a wide range of symptoms—including headaches, upset stomachs, sore muscles, chest pains, nasal congestion, watering eyes, ringing in the ears, racing heart, dizziness, flushed face, sweating hands, and shortness of breath—occurs frequently and that many if not most people experience some of these symptoms much of the time. Behavioral scientists have also found that only a small number of people experiencing such problems ever seek professional care. In most cases, the mere presence of symptoms does not prompt a person to seek professional assistance. Illness becomes an everyday typical experience, and the treated case actually represents only the tip of a "clinical iceberg." It is further evident that the experience of unexpected physiological arousal (symptoms) places an individual in a position of needing and seeking information from others to help give meaning to what he or she is experiencing. Thus, when unexpected physiological changes occur, research findings suggest that we seek out explanations or attributions from our memory and through the advice of others.

388. The answer is D. *(Kaplan, ed 4. pp 140, 340.)* Hyperthyroidism (thyrotoxicosis) is a syndrome resulting from a chronic excess of thyroid hormone (thyroxine). It may be precipitated by acute emotional stress and may even develop within hours after an emotional trauma. It is an endocrine disorder and is almost always accompanied by mental changes, in that the patient may feel tense and hyperexcitable and may be emotionally labile, with inappropriate temper outbursts, crying spells, or euphoria. Also present may be distractibility, short attention span, and impaired recent memory. Severe hyperthyroidism may result in frank psychosis, delirium, coma, and death. Thyroid disorders are seven times more frequent in women than in men, occurring most commonly in women in their third and fourth decades and in men at older ages. In contrast to the tense and hyperexcitable behaviors usually observed, a minority of patients, particularly the elderly, may be depressed, apathetic, and anorectic with chronic hyperthyroidism. Mildly hyperthyroid patients occasionally are misdiagnosed as having anxiety neuroses. Mental retardation in children is frequently associated with *hypo*thyroidism, not *hyper*thyroidism, since normal brain development requires the thyroid hormone.

389. The answer is D. *(Brody, ed 2. pp 285-288.)* Maintaining a lean body is conducive to good health and a long life. Actuarial studies have shown that obesity is associated with a diminished life expectancy. A 50-year-old man who is 50 pounds overweight has half the remaining life expectancy of a normal-weight man of the same age. Excess weight can aggravate existing health problems, causing more severe symptoms or accelerating the appearance of a disorder earlier in life than might otherwise occur. Experts in heart disease estimate that at least one-fourth of our problems with cardiovascular disease are attributable to obesity, which makes the heart and lungs work harder than normal. Although obesity is not the leading cause of hypertension, it does contribute to it, which in turn can cause death from heart and kidney disease and stroke. For example, hypertension is twice as common among the obese as among lean persons. Many people with high blood pressure are able to bring their pressure down to normal levels without drugs by losing weight and reducing their consumption of salt. Obesity also increases the risk of developing diabetes about fourfold and is associated with heart disease, blood clots, varicose veins, gout, respiratory disease, gastrointestinal disorders, gallbladder and liver disease, and arthritis of weight-bearing joints. Overweight people appear to be more clumsy, react to unexpected events more slowly, and are more likely to have accidents than normal-weight people. Compared with the general population, overweight people are more likely to die in automobile accidents. They have also been shown to be more susceptible to complications from surgery, infections, and delayed healing of wounds.

390. **The answer is D.** *(Lerner, 1984. pp 191-225.)* Even though adolescents are relatively free of illnesses and have lower rates of illness and health care utilization than children or adults, they account for over twice as many automobile accidents as adults, 20 percent of all suicides, over 600,000 pregnancies in unmarried girls per year, and a 32 percent pregnancy rate among sexually active, unmarried teenagers. They are the only age group for which the death rate is actually increasing, with a higher death rate than 20 years ago. Seventy percent of all deaths of teenagers are the result of automobile accidents or violence, both of which are increasing in frequency among adolescents while they are decreasing in the general population. The reported smoking rate for 12-to-17-year-old teenagers is 12 percent and the rate increases to 26 percent for the 17-to-18-year-old group.

391. **The answer is C.** *(Lerner, 1984. pp 195-207.)* Motor vehicle accidents are the major cause of death among adolescents and young adults. Physicians consider them to be of epidemic proportion among adolescents—in whom they account for 36 percent of all deaths. Homicide is the second leading cause of death with about 25 percent of homicides occurring in the 15-to-24-year-old group. Suicide is the third leading cause of death and is increasing for this age group, while it is decreasing for the general population. Infections and illicit drug abuse account for a relatively small number of deaths in this age group.

392. **The answer is C.** *(Lerner, 1984. pp 194-195.)* An extensive study by Korlath showed the following incidences of health concerns of adolescents: colds (70%), depression (48%), dental problems (43%), personal problems (42%), flu (40%), family problems (35%), acne (34%), eye trouble (31%), headaches (27%), weight problems (26%), nervousness (25%), and difficulty sleeping (25%). Thus, socioemotional problems equal or exceed physical problems, and all were ranked higher than such physical problems as menstrual disorders and sexual problems (e.g., birth control, urinary infections, vaginal infections, venereal disease, and pregnancy). Also, physical problems such as acne, dental problems, headaches, and obesity have prominent behavioral components, and socioemotional problems such as depression, personal and family problems, nervousness, and sleeping difficulties have related physical components. Physicians must take a broader perspective, considering and integrating biological, psychological, social, and situational factors in response to health perceptions and concerns.

393. **The answer is B (1, 3).** *(Conger, ed 3. pp 511-512.)* College students who do not drink alcohol tend to come from rural, conservative, and deeply religious (usually Protestant) backgrounds. Heavy use of alcohol is found more frequently among social science majors from metropolitan areas, particularly those who are pessimistic about their future. Heavy drinkers are more likely than nondrinkers to use nonalcoholic drugs and have a higher rate of academic failure and drop-out. Their parents are more likely to drink, as well as their friends and best friends.

394. **The answer is E (all).** *(Lerner, 1984. pp 200-204.)* Smoking is a behavior determined by multiple factors; however, a number of environmental factors have been found to place individual adolescents at greater risk of becoming regular smokers. Adolescents employed outside the home are more apt to start smoking (females having twice the risk); if both of their parents smoke they have twice the risk, less if one parent smokes, and much less if neither parent smokes; the greater the number of friends who smoke, the greater risk, especially if one's best friend smokes; adult role models (teachers, television stars, adult friends) who smoke increase the risk of the teenager smoking. Positive-image and action-oriented advertising also increases the risk, as well as individual rebelliousness, not participating in organized school and community activities, low school achievement, impatience in assuming an adult role, and need for a sense of identity.

395. **The answer is A (1, 2, 3).** *(Schneiderman, pp 439-445.)* Pain and pain-related behavior can be influenced by the environment via basic learning mechanisms. This concept has made a major contribution to the understanding and management of chronic pain. It recognizes that the pain behavior itself (the overt actions and reactions of the person) is significant in its own right, and not necessarily attributed to some underlying anxiety or conflict. Also, it emphasizes operational measurement and observation of the pain behavior itself (e.g., moaning, inactivity, use of medications), not the pain or inferred concepts as to why the person is feeling or reacting to pain. Using these concepts, the pain behavior can be conditioned as separate from the pain itself.

396. The answer is A (1, 2, 3). *(Schneiderman, pp 439-445.)* The environment can influence pain-related behavior via learning mechanisms, principally operant conditioning, respondent or classical conditioning, and modeling or observational learning. This is referred to as the learning mechanisms hypothesis. Certain rewards or secondary gains from the environment (e.g., reduced work or increased attention) are involved in operant behavior mechanisms of reward and reinforcement. The respondent conditioning mechanism involves a specific antecedent; for example, a person may link increased pain with sleep time so that the pain and preparing for sleep become associated, with the result of anticipatory anxiety and increased pain at bed time. Observational learning (or vicarious learning, or modeling) refers to learned reactions to pain as observed in parents, peers, and family or through role expectation. Thereby, one's pain-related behavior or reaction is prelearned or modeled on others.

397. The answer is E (all). *(Rosen, pp 7-10.)* A remarkable number of studies have found that schooling, marital status, income level, and even religious participation are good predictors of health and longevity. Education is associated with income, life changes, life-style, habits, knowledge, self-esteem, and other factors, all of which affect health and illness. Marriage status favors men, but both men and women gain significantly relative to unmarried or divorced persons. Religious participation generally is related to conventionality in life-style, and more positive health behaviors in respect to smoking, drinking, and other risks.

398. The answer is A (1, 2, 3). *(Kandel, ed 2. p 660.)* A recent study showed that emotional problems were the cause of 70 percent of the cases of insomnia. Depression, which is characterized by early morning awakening, was the most frequent cause of insomnia. Anxiety, positively correlated with difficulty in falling asleep, was the other most frequent cause of insomnia. The most frequent presenting complaint was insomnia, not depression, and hence it was often treated initially with sleeping pills.

399. The answer is E (all). *(Carroll, pp 352-356.)* The mechanism is not completely understood, but the health of an individual becomes more vulnerable in mourning than in normal times. This is especially true if an individual is already sick. In general, mourners tend to become ill more easily and tend to take longer to recover. Diseases that appear to occur with increased frequency during the first year of mourning (especially if it is intense) include cancer, rheumatic disease, heart disease, and kidney disease. There are also many other physical side effects, such as headaches, asthma, fatigue, indigestion, skin rashes, and palpitations.

400. The answer is A (1, 2, 3). *(Braunwald, ed 11. pp 452-454.)* Treatment with multiple medications is a major health problem in the elderly and enhances the hazard of complications from those drugs. About 90 percent of the elderly take at least one medication and the majority take two or more. Forty percent are over-the-counter drugs. It has also been found that over half of patients over age 60 make one or more medication errors during each illness. Psychotropic agents surpass all other drugs consumed in long-term care facilities (in 75 percent of institutionalized patients as opposed to 25 percent of ambulatory patients). The highest risk factors for adverse drug reactions, in addition to use of multiple drugs, include being a woman; this risk is most frequently attributed to small body size.

401.   The answer is E (all). *(Rosen, p 8.)* The social and economic characteristics of a population, such as income, education, and marital status, are better predictors of morbidity and longevity than biological or psychological markers. Sex and age, however, are the exceptions. Over the life-span, the frequency of disease and mortality increases. Also, women retain an advantage of approximately eight years over men in longevity.

402.   The answer is C (2, 4). *(Rosen, pp 219-222.)* There are a wide range of intervention strategies and technologies, many of which are very successful (e.g., 50 to 70 percent), but the relapse rate is also high, especially during the first 6 to 9 months after the behavioral change program has terminated. This emphasizes the need to continue some strategy to sustain the behavior, as one might continue to prescribe a drug for hypertension or diabetes. While the behavioral technology for changing behavior is well developed, we are not so well informed about how to prepare and motivate people to decide to adopt risk reduction and health promotion regimens. Outstanding progress has been made on identifying and modifying risk factors and risk behavior, but we know much less about health promotion, since promoting health is far more complex than eliminating risk factors and risk behaviors. Lastly, a far greater percentage of people are able to successfully initiate, complete, and maintain risk-reducing behaviors if they do so on their own. This success appears to be related to self-direction, but little is known about how this occurs, just as medicine knows little about how certain illnesses or conditions abate without medical intervention.

403.   The answer is A (1, 2, 3). *(Guthrie, ed 6. pp 159-170.)* Fat will accumulate only when the intake of energy exceeds the output of energy. The major causes of obesity have been found to be social, environmental, psychological, economic, ethnic, cultural, racial, genetic, metabolic, endocrinologic, and nutritional. Although studies have not identified any personality factors common to obese persons, the psychological makeup of obese persons has a definite influence on their difficulty in making a satisfactory weight adjustment. Some behavioral factors include life-style, life adjustment, emotional support, anxiety relief, substitute for love and security, response to or defense against tension and frustration, availability of food, comfortable environment, linking of food and hospitality, eating habits, decreased activity, and conditions under which one usually eats. Analysis of these factors and programs to change these behaviors have been found to facilitate weight control.

404. The answer is B (1, 3). *(Rosen, pp 201-214.)* An individual's beliefs are important determinants of preventive health behavior. Even though most patients with hypertension cannot determine when their blood pressure is abnormal, the majority believe they can. They are also more apt to believe that their own reading of symptoms and the fact of feeling better are more valid than their physician's instructions or reassurances. As a result, many patients will stop or change treatment on the basis of their feelings and symptoms. If patients have the belief that they can control their health outcome, they are more apt to try to be more successful in changing such health behaviors as smoking, diet, and exercise to prevent or to cure an illness. Older patients are more apt to believe that they can enhance their health by controlling their emotions (anger, anxiety, and depression) and staying mentally active. Younger people place more value on vigorous exercise to promote health and prevent illness.

405. The answer is A (1, 2, 3). *(Last, ed 12. pp 985, 1056-1066.)* Research findings on the use of alcoholic beverages show that the life span of an alcoholic is on the average shortened by 10 to 12 years. Alcohol is considered to be a contributory cause in half of all deaths resulting from automobile accidents. The current use rate of alcohol is 70 percent for young adults in the age range of 18 to 25 years and 55 percent for older adults, 26 years or more in age. Recent research on the behavior and educational treatment of problem drinking and alcoholism has shown that total, complete, and permanent abstinence is no longer considered a necessary treatment objective. The total abstinence treatment was based on the belief that alcoholism is a physical disease characterized by craving for alcohol and loss of control over drinking during periods of intoxication. The disease model justified abstinence because one cannot allow a sick person to have access to the agent that causes the sickness. Abstinence was also an exquisitely simple treatment goal to define and monitor. Although total abstinence is appropriate in some instances, more recent empirical studies of the drinking behavior of alcoholics supports the use of the learning model. Various behavioral therapies are employed, such as the use of rewards rather than punishments and the pursuit of controlled social drinking rather than total abstinence as a therapy goal. The degree of dependence on alcohol is an important underlying factor.

406. The answer is E (all). *(Feuerstein, pp 225-230.)* Psychosocial variables have been demonstrated to exert some modest control over lung function and the clinical course of asthma. Some asthmatics are more sensitive to psychological stimuli, especially behavioral intervention for reducing stress. Systematic desensitization requires that the patient construct a hierarchy of situations or stimuli that trigger or aggravate an asthma attack. By relaxing and presenting the threatening situations in hierarchical sequence, the patient becomes desensitized to the situation. Implosion represents repeated exposures to distressing stimuli (a kind of flooding) to accomplish a desensitization of the patient to the distressing stimuli. Systematic desensitization and implosion are particularly effective in the treatment of asthma panic. Family therapy incorporates the social context of the sick patient within the family and identifies transactional and conflict patterns that precipitate or aggravate asthma. Relaxation therapy is less effective, but does produce significant results.

407. The answer is E (all). *(Last, ed 12. pp 983-991.)* Recognition of the influence of individual behavior on health goes back many years. The major causes of death, serious illness, and disability in the United States today are chronic disease and violence. Chronic diseases accounted for 76 percent of all deaths in 1976. Accidents, suicide, and homicide accounted for another 8 percent. Another measure of the relative impact of various diseases and lethal forces is the concept of "potential years of life lost," which highlights the loss to society as a result of youthful or early death. The most recent life expectancy tables indicate that three categories—diseases of the circulatory system, cancer, and accidents and violence—account for about 72 percent of the potential years of life lost in the United States. Two chronic disease categories—diseases of the circulatory and musculoskeletal system—account for 38 percent of conditions causing disability and limitations of major activity. Behind most chronic diseases, disabilities, and premature deaths are many environmental and behavioral factors, potentially amenable or susceptible to change or prevention. Although the etiology is usually multidimensional, it is now recognized that environmental threats and individual behavior play a major role. It is estimated that about 80 percent of all cancer among men and 75 percent among women is attributable to environmental or behavioral factors or a combination of both. This percentage represents a great "prevention potential." Among the individual and societal life-style patterns that constitute the major behavioral risk factors involved in chronic disease and severe disability are cigarette smoking, alcohol and other drug abuse, nutritional abuse, lack of adequate physical activity, irresponsible use of motor vehicles, irresponsible use of guns and other manifestations of violence, the apparent decline of family health and social supports, sexual promiscuity or carelessness about contraception, and excessive television viewing. Information alone is insufficient for change, so health education must be directed at devising the most effective strategies for changing and then maintaining the individual and group behavior that promotes health and prevents disease.

408. The answer is A (1, 2, 3). *(Last, ed 12. pp 1402-1411.)* In 1980, 23,970 lives were lost owing to homicide. This represented more than 690,000 potential years of life lost, with homicide ranking fourth in that measure. Homicide was the eleventh leading cause of death overall. Homicide was the leading cause of death for black or minority young people (15 to 34 years old). Possibly many additional homicide deaths were misclassified as "accidents" or "cause of death unknown." Homicide takes its greatest toll among minorities (44 percent), males (76 percent), and the young (56 percent). Friends or acquaintances accounted for the greatest number of homicides (45 percent) and nearly one-third of those were committed by a member of the family. The most frequently used weapon in homicide is a handgun (40 percent); other guns (24 percent), knives (17 percent), and other means (19 percent) account for the remaining homicides.

409. The answer is A (1, 2, 3). *(Rosen, pp 303-304.)* The link between behavior and cancer progression is becoming more established, especially for the relationship between inability to express emotion (e.g., hostility) and cancer. Sandra Levy is finding that negatively reactive patients with metastatic breast cancer live significantly longer than passive patients. On the other hand, overly cooperative, bland, and passive cancer patients in the face of stress have a shorter life-span. Also, patients with breast cancer who are married or who are a part of an intact social network have an increased survival rate.

410. The answer is E (all). *(Rosen, pp 132-133.)* In the type A behavior pattern, the joyless striving characteristic is regarded by Friedman and Rosenman as representing a constant struggle for recognition and reward in order to overcome fears of inadequacy and insecurity. As such, emotional exhaustion, feelings of despair, hopelessness, and depression can be recognized as prodromes of type A individuals just prior to their myocardial infarction and frequently sudden death. Such chronic striving can represent an attempt to overcome the underlying feelings of depression.

411. The answer is E (all). *(Last, ed 12. pp 984, 1000-1014.)* The health consequences of smoking behavior are well established and clearly understood. The term smoking behavior is used because smoking is a behavioral act. Respective studies show that smokers, especially cigarette smokers, are much more likely than nonsmokers to die from a large number of diseases. Among these are diseases of the heart, bronchitis/emphysema, arteriosclerosis, and cancers of the lung, oral cavity, larynx, pancreas, bladder, esophagus, and kidney. Other diseases and disorders caused or affected by smoking behavior are cancer of the upper gastrointestinal tract, peptic ulcers, and adverse effects on the fetus. Increases in total mortality of cigarette smokers in prospective studies vary from 30 to 80 percent, depending partly on the age groups studied. An overall risk of 60 percent greater than the mortality of nonsmokers is considered a reasonable estimate. This results in a reduced life expectation of cigarette smokers of 5 to 6 years. The reduction in life expectation increases directly with the number of cigarettes smoked. Current estimates (1977) show that smoking-related deaths in the United States represent approximately 18 percent of the total mortality distribution of the population. Eighty-five percent of the deaths from bronchitis/emphysema and 87 percent of the deaths from lung cancer are smoking-related. Smoking is known to double the risk of having a myocardial infarction.

412. The answer is C (2, 4). *(Lindzey, ed 3. pp 809-810.)* Social context and peer pressure are most important both in acquiring a habit of substance abuse and in maintaining it. The social context has been shown to be of primary importance in maintaining a habit of substance abuse, even for addicted heroin users. Substance abuse includes such addictive behaviors as smoking, drug abuse, and alcohol abuse. Peer pressure is especially effective with teenagers in initiating, terminating, and avoiding substance abuse, especially with cigarette smoking. The percentage of teenage smokers is still increasing, especially among teenage females. Attempts by such pioneers as Richard Evans to use peer pressure to prevent smoking among teenagers have been relatively effective. Becoming a teenage smoker has some immediate value, such as being accepted by one's peers, feeling more mature or adult, and defying authority figures. Fear arousal and traditional health education methods have had very limited effects on smoking and other addictive behaviors.

413. The answer is E (all). *(U.S. Public Health Service, 81-1232, pp 31-33.)* Survival is not the sole criterion for evaluating pregnancy outcomes. Many conditions that may lead to an infant's death also carry potential hazardous consequences when the outcome is not fatal. The most significant characteristic associated with a poor pregnancy outcome is low birth weight, usually defined as less than 5½ pounds or 2,500 g. Low birth weight infants face a fiftyfold greater chance of dying before 1 month of age and are five times more likely to die between 1 month and 1 year of age than are infants of normal birth weight. They are also more likely to have serious congenital anomalies or other severe impairments. Low birth weight babies are likely to have a greater rate of developmental problems than are heavier babies. In 1977, 235,000 low birth weight infants were born in the United States. This represented 7.1 percent of all live births. The incidence of low birth weight morbidity and mortality is most frequently related to poor nutrition, smoking, stress, and poor physical condition. The incidence of low birth weight was more than twice as high for black infants as it was for white infants (12.8 percent and 5.9 percent, respectively). Nearly all the difference in neonatal mortality between white and black infants can be attributed to difference in birth weight distribution. The incidence of low birth weight declined by 14 percent between 1965 and 1977, whereas infant mortality declined by 43 percent. Much of this improved outcome for low birth weight infants has been attributed to advances in neonatology and the establishment of regionalized perinatal networks.

414. The answer is E (all). *(Matarazzo, pp 73-78, 1003-1005.)* During adolescence, there is a marked increase in the number of suicides. Adolescents 15 to 19 years of age accounted for 6 percent of the 25,000 suicides in the United States in 1976. Boys are three times more likely to commit suicide than are girls, and boys typically choose more violent acts than the more passive methods used by girls. Adolescents also account for more than 12 percent of all suicide attempts, with 90 percent of the attempts being made by females. It is thought that suicide attempts represent an adolescent's final call for help and attention. These attempts are all too often successful. During the period between 1950 and 1975, the rate of suicide for males between the ages of 15 and 19 increased from 5 per 100,000 population to 15. During the same period of time, the suicide rate for females of the same age group went from approximately 2 to 5 per 100,000 population. Studies show that suicidal adolescents appear to have failed to identify with significant others in their environment, were unable to remember any feelings of closeness, emotional attachment, or identification with adults, and felt that their situation could not change.

415. **The answer is E (all).** *(Last, ed 12. pp 999-1017.)* Intensive scientific studies begun in the 1940s have clearly established the health hazards associated with the use of tobacco products, particularly cigarettes. The overall mortality risk for smokers compared with nonsmokers is 60 percent greater. Each cigarette smoked shortens the smoker's life span by about 5.5 minutes. Studies in the 1950s showed that smokers were much more likely than nonsmokers to die from a large number of diseases. Lung cancer, cardiovascular diseases, and emphysema are three of the more significant diseases associated with smoking. The risk of dying of lung cancer, for example, is between 8 and 15 times higher in cigarette smokers than in nonsmokers. More recent studies have led to the realization that there is a serious impact of smoking pollution on the health of nonsmokers. For example, children whose parents smoke have a higher incidence of respiratory infections and impaired function than those whose parents do not smoke.

416. **The answer is C (2, 4).** *(Last, ed 12. pp 985, 1039-1043.)* Alcohol abuse is the second most frequent form of drug dependence after tobacco. It directly affects an estimated 2.5 to 5 percent of the United States population. In addition, their families, employers, and coworkers are directly and indirectly affected. With about half the annual traffic deaths being related to alcohol use and abuse, a major physical health and disability problem is generated. The annual economic loss associated with alcohol abuse was estimated to be over $50 billion annually, which was even greater than the cost of tobacco-related disease and death. Drinking alcoholic beverages has generally become a socially acceptable form of activity, but its adverse effect on health and behavior is severe. Alcohol use contributes to a number of disease conditions and reduces the efficiency of productive activity. The percentage of families with problem-drinking men is highest (21 percent) in the young age group (21-29 years) and falls to approximately 11 percent in the older age group of 50 to 59 years of age. The increased use of psychoactive drugs, especially among the younger age group, has led to a major effort to bring such drug dependence into the mainstream of modern medicine, public health, and medical education. Furthermore, there is a renewed recognition of both the physical and psychological dependence common with the use of alcohol and tobacco.

417. **The answer is E (all).** *(Braunwald, ed 11. pp 2108-2109.)* The diagnosis of alcoholism is difficult, but general criteria include four situations: when an individual ignores early warning signs such as alcohol-related problems in marriage and then goes on to an alcohol-related marital separation or divorce; or when a person is fired or laid-off because of an alcohol-related problem; or when there are two or more arrests related to alcohol; or when there is evidence that alcohol has harmed one's health, such as cardiomyopathy, cirrhosis, or alcoholic hepatitis, including signs of alcohol withdrawal.

418. The answer is E (all). *(Rosen, pp 51-52.)* The developing fetus can be severely affected by the mother's consumption of alcohol. The condition called fetal alcohol syndrome (FAS) is estimated to occur in 1 in every 750 to 1,000 live births. Mothers who are heavy or moderate drinkers are more apt to bear children with reduced physical growth, mental retardation, and central nervous system damage and to have increased rates of spontaneous abortion and stillbirth. It is estimated that in the state of New York alone, infants born with alcohol-related birth defects in a single year will cost the economy $155,000,000 in life-time care.

419. The answer is A (1, 2, 3). *(Last, ed 12. pp 977-978.)* What patients know, believe, and think about their illness affects the symptoms they think to be important, what they see as serious, and what they think they should do. Their social roles and personal desires often lead them to deny an illness. They often ignore symptoms for a long period before taking action. Fear about particular illnesses that may be of life-threatening character often cause them to deny the existence of the symptoms or their seriousness. Also, when their level of fear exceeds their capacity to cope, denial is a very likely result. The psychological process of secondary gain will also produce a postponement of action, but is not usually associated with denial. Health educators need to help people bypass the usual hypothesis-testing of the cause of symptoms and help them take action by consulting a physician.

420. The answer is A (1, 2, 3). *(Matarazzo, pp 496-503.)* Most studies dealing with the effects of exercise on depression have demonstrated significant improvements in the subject's mood state, particularly in depression. Exercise was as effective as time-limited psychotherapy, meditation, or group psychotherapy. Exercise fostered a sense of mastery, a positive self-image, an increased peripheral and cerebral blood flow, increased oxygenation, increased levels of catecholamines (norepinephrine and epinephrine), and some cathartic relief. While the studies have been mainly correlational rather than causative and they may have been influenced by a self-selecting bias, the evidence is considered more than suggestive. The expectancy and demand characteristics associated with exercise are very powerful.

421. The answer is C (2, 4). *(Rosen, p 112.)* There are many claims of health benefits from exercise, but the greatest scientific evidence supports the prevention of coronary heart disease, the maintenance of optimal body weight and body composition, and the normalization of fat and carbohydrate metabolism. There is also good support for the prevention of hypertension, osteoporosis, and low back pain and for improved psychological status. While exercise has not been shown to prevent such diseases as type I diabetes, chronic obstructive lung disease, renal failure, or arthritis, it has been shown to result in clinical improvement of these and other diseases.

422. The answer is E (all). *(Rosen, pp 117-118.)* Exercise has a major effect on the amount of fat in relation to lean tissue and body weight. Exercise of moderate intensity can result in an increase in energy expenditure of 300 kcal for 30 minutes of activity. Also the metabolic rate remains elevated for several hours after physical activity, which further increases the contribution of exercise to weight loss. Exercise is important in the elderly as it helps retain muscle mass. Exercise also contributes to general weight loss, especially when combined with calorie restriction, as it causes a greater proportion of weight loss to be from adipose tissue.

423. The answer is A (1, 2, 3). *(Hamburg, pp 99-107.)* Cigarette smoking is a powerful addiction; it is estimated that about 60 percent of smokers have tried to quit and another 30 percent want to quit. While nicotine may be the major pharmacological reinforcer and behavioral factors play a role in the reinforcement of the addiction, behavioral factors have been demonstrated to play a major role in the initiation of the smoking habit itself, the day-to-day fluctuations in smoking, and the difficulty of maintaining abstinence after one has quit. Behavioral factors also play a major role in the situations in which smoking occurs and in the choice of cigarette brands. Of the estimated 30 million smokers who try to quit each year, only about 3 million achieve long-term abstinence. A physician's advice has a low 1-year abstinence result, except for patients recovering from a recent heart attack, in which the 1-year abstinence is about 50 percent.

424. The answer is B (1, 3). *(Braunwald, ed 11. pp 2093-2096.)* Twin, family, and adoptive studies have shown that schizophrenia has a significant and primary genetic basis. Even though psychosocial factors are regarded as secondary, the stress-diathesis model incorporates a host of stressful factors that may precipitate a psychotic state in a high-risk individual. The stress can be the result of specific illnesses, social or psychological, environmental, or chemical, such as that from use of PCP or amphetamines. Also, specific hallucinogens may precipitate a psychotic episode that is indistinguishable from schizophrenia. There is no specific schizophrenia-prone personality type, even though a small percentage of individuals with a schizoid and paranoid personality disorder seem to be more vulnerable to developing schizophrenic disorders. Lower socioeconomic status does correlate with a higher incidence of schizophrenia.

425. The answer is E (all). *(Steptoe, pp 302-303.)* After myocardial infarction a patient experiences many psychosocial and physical responses, even a full year after he acute attack. The most frequent response is a change in mood, leading to depression and anxiety. Also, a majority report experiencing moderate physical distress, extensive disturbances in subjective states, contradictions between patients and their families in assessing the patient's level of activity, the perception of themselves as handicapped, and personal lives that have not returned to normal. These factors must be recognized in order to achieve a successful rehabilitation.

426-429. The answers are: 426-E, 427-C, 428-B, 429-A. *(Braunwald, ed 11. pp 164-165, 1456-1458, 1520-1522, 1611-1613.)* Sickle cell anemia is a congenital hemolytic anemia seen most frequently among, and hence characterized as a condition of, the black population. About 0.15 percent of black children in the United States have sickle cell anemia. It has a lower prevalence in adults because of decreased life expectancy.

Phenylketonuria is an autosomal recessive metabolic disorder. It is associated with severe mental retardation and, less frequently, with other neurologic manifestations such as psychomotor symptoms. No abnormalities are apparent at birth, but treatment in early infancy may prevent retardation.

Osteoarthritis, known also as degenerative joint disease, is most often an affliction of advancing years. Wear and tear processes seem to be the major etiologic factor; certain occupations and hobbies, particularly those involving joint trauma, appear to be causally related to the development of osteoarthritis. Forty million Americans have radiologic evidence of degenerative joint disease, including 85 percent of persons over the age of 70.

Although dental decay has links with heredity and a direct relationship to age, the most important factor associated with tooth decay at every age is lack of attention and poor oral hygiene, most frequently occurring in poverty or lower socioeconomic situations. Unless treated, this infection of enamel and underlying dentin in due course extends to involvement of the dental pulp and frequently results in loss of the affected tooth.

430-433. The answers are: 430-B, 431-A, 432-C, 433-E. *(Williams, SJ, ed 2. pp 49-63.)* Several major characteristics of a community are directly related to health status and to health care systems or other approaches devised to meet perceived health needs. The nature and distribution of the present system of medical care in the United States are products of a political process determined in turn by economic and social class structure. These determinants of the health care system place power in a community's dominant individuals to decide how and to whom health services are distributed.

Income has a direct relationship to health. Such critical measures of community health as maternal mortality, prenatal and infant mortality, life span, disability, and hypertension are worse in all age categories among individuals who are poor. Unlike the affluent, the poor cannot buy good health services. When the data are adjusted for health status, the lower socioeconomic groups still have fewer visits to physicians than do higher income groups. Primary care programs reach less than one-third of the medically underserved.

The elderly at every income level in every social class demonstrate a proportionally higher need for health services than other population groups. Increasing expenditures for Medicare relate to increasing costs. The elderly continue to suffer disproportionate neglect on the basis of income, needs, and services available.

Individuals' perceptions of their own health status can be influenced by sociocultural factors, including their particular community's technologic prowess. Indeed, all these factors shape an individual's attitude toward health, an attitude that, in turn, eventually governs that person's response to his or her own health needs and use of the health services available. Level of education and income is related to the use of preventive services and preventive behavior.

434-439. The answers are: 434-A, 435-B, 436-A, 437-C, 438-D, 439-C. *(Kandel, ed 2. pp 715-719.)* Major unipolar depression and bipolar (manic depressive) disorders are affective disorders, involving a disturbance of mood or feeling tone. Both are related to an intrinsic regulatory defect involving, at least in part, the hypothalamus because of its regulation of mood, sexual drive, sleep, and autonomic and motor activity.

For unipolar depression, the average age of onset is about 40 years and the incidence for women is about two to three times greater than for men. It also tends to recur about four times during the next 20 years. The depression usually lasts 4 to 12 months, and it is estimated that about 4 percent (8 million people) of the U.S. population suffers from it.

Bipolar (manic depressive) disorder causes both depressive and manic episodes and affects men and women about equally. The typical age of onset is about 30 years, and it is clinically similar to unipolar depression. The manic phase lasts about a week or longer. It is also recurrent and the episodes of depression and mania occur about twice as often over a 20-year period as in unipolar depression.

Neither unipolar nor bipolar depression can be related to significant psychosocial precipitating factors in at least 60 percent of the episodes, and both are relatively unresponsive to conventional psychotherapy and environmental change. Treatment with medication is frequently effective. There also appears to be a strong genetic predisposition for both unipolar and bipolar depressions. Genetic studies have shown them to be not completely distinct but probably part of a spectrum of depressive illness; the unipolar depression may represent a milder form and the bipolar depression the more severe form of the same disorder. Chromosome number 11 has been demonstrated to be related to bipolar depression.

Health Care Systems

DIRECTIONS: Each question below contains five suggested responses. Select the **one best** response to each question.

440. Patients seek the services of "nonscientific," in preference to "scientific," systems of healing primarily because these services are

(A) less costly
(B) more available
(C) more efficacious
(D) more supportive
(E) none of the above

441. Which of the following prevention models is most frequently used to prevent the development of alcoholism and problem drinking?

(A) Public health
(B) Sociocultural/environmental
(C) Distribution of consumption
(D) Biological
(E) Psychological

442. The lowest infant mortality among industrialized countries is found in

(A) Finland
(B) Sweden
(C) Switzerland
(D) Netherlands
(E) United States

443. The folk medical care system employed by many Mexicans and Mexican-Americans is known as

(A) medico
(B) allopathy
(C) voodoo
(D) soma
(E) curanderismo

444. The form of treatment that most resembles curanderismo in its techniques of therapy is

(A) allopathy
(B) homeopathy
(C) osteopathy
(D) chiropractic
(E) spiritual healing

445. All the following statements about Professional Standards Review Organizations are correct EXCEPT that they

(A) were created under the provisions of the 1972 Social Security Amendments
(B) formulate their own criteria, norms, and standards for their activities
(C) certify the appropriateness of patient admissions to the hospital
(D) mandate patient discharge when a hospital stay is inappropriately long
(E) review hospital medical care to determine its quality

446. Most mental health care authorities agree that the recent trend toward community-based treatment of individuals who have emotional disorders, as opposed to their incarceration in public mental institutions, can be ascribed principally to

(A) improved therapeutic results when treatment is available within a patient's community
(B) the development of preventive measures for various mental illnesses
(C) the use of new drugs that allow many emotionally disturbed patients to function outside an institution
(D) an increasing willingness by general hospitals to accept mentally disturbed patients
(E) the 1961 report of the Joint Commission on Mental Illness and Health strongly recommending community mental health programs

447. All the following statements about individuals of lower socioeconomic status and their attitudes toward health are true EXCEPT that

(A) their medical needs are greater
(B) they are less concerned about their health
(C) they have a chronically low utilization rate of health services
(D) their health-seeking behaviors do not change even when financial barriers are removed
(E) they are more alienated from society and medical institutions

448. The single most significant source of preventable morbidity and premature mortality is

(A) environmental pollution
(B) crime and homicide
(C) auto and home accidents
(D) poor nutrition
(E) cigarette smoking

449. Data from the periodic National Health Interview Surveys show the following statements about ambulatory health care services to be true EXCEPT that

(A) the national average for visits to physicians is about 5 visits per person per year
(B) outpatient visits are increasing at a more rapid rate than inpatient admissions
(C) there is a positive relationship between annual family income and the number of physician contacts per person per year
(D) there are generally higher rates of ambulatory physician contacts by females than by males
(E) respiratory system disease is the most frequent diagnostic category for visits to the physician's office, followed by circulatory system disease

450. Studies of the economics of health care show that all the following statements are true EXCEPT that

(A) between 1940 and 1982, the percent of GNP spent on health more than doubled
(B) per capita expenditures for health care increased nearly tenfold between 1950 and 1977
(C) government expenditures for health care have increased nearly 2,000 percent since 1950
(D) current health expenditures by the federal government represent 13 percent of the total federal budget
(E) the federal government contributes 72 percent of the funds in the total health care field

451. Economic benefits of health promotion programs to the employer are seen in all the following areas EXCEPT

(A) cessation of smoking
(B) worker absenteeism
(C) worker morale
(D) life and disability insurance costs
(E) company pension fund costs

452. International statistics on the per capita consumption of absolute alcohol in liters show which country to rate the highest?

(A) Finland
(B) United States
(C) U.S.S.R.
(D) Spain
(E) France

453. Between 1950 and 1980, the greatest total percentage increase in per capita consumption of alcoholic beverages was in

(A) Finland
(B) France
(C) East German Democratic Republic
(D) Netherlands
(E) Poland

454. All the following statements about the early history of medical education in the United States are correct EXCEPT that *(in 1256)*

(A) the first medical school in the United States was established in 1783 at Harvard University

(B) the American Medical Association (AMA) at its founding in 1847 had as a primary goal the reform of medical education

(C) the Association of American Medical Colleges (AAMC) was organized in 1876 as part of the effort to improve the quality of medical education

(D) in 1902, the *Journal of the American Medical Association (JAMA)* began publishing medical school failure statistics on state licensing board examinations

(E) in 1905, only five medical schools required any college preparation for admission

455. Which of the following health profession schools has shown the greatest percentage increase in enrollment of women over the past 15 years?

(A) Optometry
(B) Pharmacology
(C) Dentistry
(D) Medicine
(E) Veterinary

456. Specialty boards play a major role in American medicine. All the following statements about the history of specialty boards are true EXCEPT that

(A) the first specialty board, the American Board for Ophthalmic Examination, was incorporated in 1917 and renamed the American Board of Ophthalmology in 1933

(B) when the Advisory Board for American Specialties was established in 1933, there were only four certifying boards

(C) the greatest growth in the number of specialty boards occurred in the 1950s

(D) the American Board of Family Practice was established in 1969

(E) in 1973, less than half the physicians practicing in the United States were diplomates of one or more of the 22 specialty boards

457. All the following statements about utilization of health care services are true EXCEPT that

(A) the differential in the utilization of health care services between the white and black population has narrowed in recent years
(B) persons from high-income families seek preventive care about twice as often as they seek diagnosis and treatment
(C) persons from low-income families seek preventive care at about the same rate as they seek diagnosis and treatment
(D) many more females than males visit community mental health centers
(E) hospital admissions rates have an inverse relationship with family income

458. All the following statements concerning health care for the elderly are true EXCEPT that

(A) demands on the health care system are expected to increase for the over-65 age group
(B) acute diseases are expected to increase in all segments of the over-65 age group
(C) females have been the heaviest users of the health care system
(D) the sex differential in human longevity is the cumulative result of excessive male mortality throughout the life-span
(E) mortality among the elderly has shown a decline over the past 15 years

459. All the following statements about nursing homes are correct EXCEPT that

(A) the average age of the residents of nursing homes is 80 or over
(B) in 1977, female residents outnumbered male residents by more than 2 to 1
(C) widowed persons and never-married persons outnumber married persons or divorced persons as residents in nursing homes
(D) many more patients enter nursing homes by transfer from general hospitals than from their residences
(E) chronic conditions or impairments found in nursing home residents in order of prevalence are senility, arthritis or rheumatism, heart trouble, and mental illness

460. Which of the following is the leading consumer of health care dollars?

(A) Cardiovascular disease
(B) Cancer
(C) Gastrointestinal disease
(D) Respiratory disease
(E) Accidents

DIRECTIONS: Each question below contains four suggested responses of which **one or more** is correct. Select

A	if	**1, 2, and 3**	are correct
B	if	**1 and 3**	are correct
C	if	**2 and 4**	are correct
D	if	**4**	is correct
E	if	**1, 2, 3, and 4**	are correct

461. Recent statistics on ambulatory care visits in the United States indicate which of the following?

(1) The number of yearly visits increases with age
(2) The number of yearly visits is higher in urban areas than in rural areas
(3) The number of yearly visits decreases as income level increases
(4) The number of reported sicknesses decreases with increased income level

462. True statements about infant mortality include which of the following?

(1) Black infant mortality in the U.S. is about twice as high as for whites
(2) Finland has one of the highest infant mortalities of all European countries
(3) Infant mortality in the U.S. is about one-third the 1950 rate
(4) the U.S. ranks eighth compared with all countries

463. True statements in regard to women receiving first trimester prenatal care in the U.S. include that

(1) in 1970, less than 55 percent of all women received prenatal care
(2) from 1980 to 1984 the percentage remained about the same
(3) from 1980 to 1984 the percentage of black women receiving prenatal care has increased faster than that of white women
(4) from 1970 to 1980 the percentage of all women receiving prenatal care increased about 12 percent

464. True statements regarding the deinstitutionalization of patients in state mental hospitals since 1955 include which of the following?

(1) It has been attributed to the improved treatment programs in state mental hospitals
(2) It provided a last resort for one class of society's rejected mentally ill population
(3) It resulted in an increased public investment in mental health
(4) It resulted in local, state, and federal agencies taking comprehensive responsibility for psychiatric and social services for the chronically mentally ill

465. Native-American healers are responsible for discovering

(1) the cure for scurvy
(2) oral contraception
(3) the use of antibiotics
(4) more than 200 drugs now officially listed in the National Formulary

466. A health maintenance organization is characterized by which of the following key principles?

(1) Provision of comprehensive medical care to its enrolled members
(2) Provision of comprehensive medical care with emphasis on efficiency and economy
(3) Voluntary enrollment of members who pay a fixed amount regardless of the services received
(4) Strong emphasis on preventive health services

467. Major reasons for the increasing cost of a hospital bed per patient day over the past decade include the

(1) implementation of Medicare and Medicaid
(2) wage increases won by professional and technical hospital employees
(3) maintenance of underutilized separate hospital services rather than merging them into regional units
(4) higher fees charged by physicians for taking care of hospitalized patients

468. The group practice of medicine may be characterized as having which of the following effects?

(1) Increases the quality of medical care because of increased attention paid to preventive medicine techniques
(2) Provides time for postgraduate study and holidays without resulting in loss of income for physician members
(3) Incurs some loss of individual freedom of action on the part of physician members
(4) Provides an average income for participating physicians that exceeds the average earned in private practice

469. There will be an increased demand for and utilization of health care services over the next 15 years because of which of the following?

(1) An increasing number of elderly consuming a larger share of health care resources
(2) A decreasing number of males compared with number of females
(3) Improved educational and income levels of the elderly
(4) Increased acute care needs of high-risk elderly

SUMMARY OF DIRECTIONS

A	B	C	D	E
1, 2, 3 only	1, 3 only	2, 4 only	4 only	All are correct

470. True statements about the nursing profession include that

(1) nearly three-fourths of all working registered nurses are employed in hospitals and nursing homes

(2) less than one-half the potentially employable registered nurses in the United States are working full-time

(3) hospitals, the major employers of registered nurses, report a very high turnover rate, often as high as 50 percent of the nursing staff annually

(4) the total number of registered nurses in practice decreased between 1960 and 1974

471. The principles of the hospice movement include which of the following?

(1) Acceptance of death as a logical part of life

(2) Self-determination

(3) Importance of family support

(4) Control of pain only when severe

Questions 480-482

Match the descriptions below with appropriate medical problem.

(A) Neoplasms
(B) Circulatory disorders
(C) Mental disorders
(D) Musculoskeletal disorders
(E) None of the above

480. The greatest number of Social Security disability awards for women

481. The greatest number of Social Security disability awards for men and women combined

482. The most rapidly increasing rate of social security disability awards

Questions 483-486

For each of the percentage changes in mortality between 1970 and 1984, select the disease with which it is associated.

(A) Diseases of the heart
(B) Malignant neoplasms
(C) Chronic obstructive pulmonary diseases
(D) Cerebrovascular diseases
(E) None of the above

483. Increased by 3 percent

484. Increased by 34 percent

485. Decreased by 28 percent

486. Decreased by 50 percent

DIRECTIONS: Each group of questions below consists of lettere
lowed by a set of numbered items. For each numbered item select t
heading with which it is **most** closely associated. Each lettered headin
once, more than once, or not at all.

Questions 472-475

For each description below, select
the health care delivery system that
matches it most closely.

    (A) Local health departments
    (B) Hospitals
    (C) Group practice
    (D) Health maintenance organiza-
        tions
    (E) Community mental health
        centers

472. Participating physicians are salaried to treat patients who regularly in-
vest a set amount for comprehensive
health care

473. Health service functions are varied, but emphasize prevention and public health measures

474. Primary concern is to provide a
number of specialized services to seriously ill patients

475. Incentives are provided to minimize the cost of health service delivery

Questions 476-479

For each health care pl
scribed, select the payment
which it is most closely asso

    (A) Medicare
    (B) National Health Insu
    (C) Medicaid
    (D) Blue Cross
    (E) Blue Shield

476. A compulsory hospital in
plan whose cost is shared by en
ees and employers through Soci
curity payroll taxes

477. A prepayment insurance pl
providing limited coverage of hos
costs on a nonprofit basis for indi
als or groups

478. A grant-in-aid program whos
costs are shared by the federal and
state governments for all low-incom
persons

479. A prepayment supplementary
medical insurance program to pay phy
sicians' fees in hospitals, surgery, and
emergency care

Health Care Systems
Answers

440. The answer is D. *(Mechanic, ed 2. pp 418-422.*) Although cost and availability may contribute to a patient's decision to seek "nonscientific" health care, the main attraction of such treatment is that it more often serves a patient's psychological needs than do "scientific" systems of health care. "Scientific" medicine frequently contradicts patients' cultural beliefs and expectations and ignores their psychological plight in the bargain.

441. The answer is A. *(Rosen, pp 34-50.)* The public health model of prevention is an epidemiological model requiring knowledge of and attention to the host, the agent, and the environment. It emphasizes the importance of a multifaceted attack on the multifaceted problem of alcoholism and is the most prevalent model used in an attempt to understand and treat alcoholism and problem drinking. The sociocultural/environmental model emphasizes the importance of efforts to alter prevailing social norms and attitudes toward alcohol to effect prevention. The distribution of consumption model of prevention stresses efforts to reduce per capita consumption of alcohol, thus reducing the proportion of heavy drinkers. The biological model proposes to identify biological factors that impact on alcohol use and abuse. The psychological model attempts to establish psychological factors and poor mental health as causative and preventable mechanisms.

442. The answer is A. *(Matarazzo, pp 42, 1006-1009. U.S. Public Health Service, 87-1232. pp 1, 85, 94.)* The lowest infant mortality in 1984 was in Finland with 6.5 deaths per 1,000 live births. The next lowest was Japan, followed by Sweden, Switzerland, Norway, Denmark, France, and Canada. The United States infant mortality of 10.8 per 1,000 live births was the lowest ever recorded in United States history, but is still ranked sixteenth among industrialized countries. This high infant mortality exists in spite of our high health care costs and more than 4 million health care professionals.

443. The answer is E. *(Twaddle, ed 2. pp 175-176.)* Curanderismo is a very popular and widely used system of folk medicine. It is a blend of Native-American medicine, Mexican folk medicine, African folk medicine, and European medieval medicine. This health care system is an important source of cultural solidarity and pride for practitioner and client alike. Indeed, the social and cultural aspects of curanderismo may well overshadow the practical concerns of actually getting well.

444. The answer is D. *(Twaddle, ed 2. p 175.)* Curanderismo, like chiropractic, stresses manipulation and massage of body parts as a major part of its therapeutic technology. However, curanderismo also enlists the aid of various medicines and poultices, including mood-changing drugs. Manipulation and massage are important in helping to establish rapport between physician and patient. Indeed, the importance of "laying on" of hands is recognized by virtually all effective systems of the curative arts.

445. The answer is D. *(Williams, SJ, ed 2. pp 207-208.)* The Social Security Amendments of 1972 provide for local Professional Standards Review Organizations (PSROs) to judge the quality of medical care delivery on the basis of standards formulated by a local PSRO in accordance with regional norms. PSROs are charged with certifying the appropriateness both of hospital admissions and of length of stay; they also are responsible for reviewing the quality of hospital care. A PSRO has no authority either to prevent admissions to or to mandate discharges from a hospital.

446. The answer is C. *(Grant, ed 3. pp 200-202, 210-212.)* The old approach of treating mentally ill people in large, isolated institutions is becoming outmoded largely because of the effectiveness of new psychotropic drugs that enable many disturbed individuals to function normally. The success of these drugs resulted in the recommendations in 1961 of the Joint Commission on Mental Illness and Health to increase the utilization of community facilities in treating mental illness. As a result, general hospitals have become more active in mental health therapy and community mental health centers have developed to support mental patients in a functional atmosphere, in addition to taking steps at a local level to prevent mental illness.

447. The answer is B. *(Counte, pp 21-24, 38-46.)* Lower income persons have a chronically low utilization rate of medical care facilities. They have a greater need for medical care and are more concerned about their health, yet they exhibit greater tolerance or endurance of symptoms. The lower utilization rates are often explained on the basis of the inadequate financial resources; the "culture of poverty," in which the poor are more apt to be alienated from society and medical institutions; and the barriers that the poor encounter, such as the greater distances from medical care facilities, the longer waits and impersonal care, the fragmented services, and a lack of understanding of how to use the system. An interesting finding is that the provision of financial assistance packages and improved access to prepaid programs does not significantly change the health-seeking behavior patterns. This would suggest the role of certain social, psychological, and cultural factors in the problem.

448. The answer is E. *(Last, ed 12. pp 999-1014.)* Each U.S. Surgeon General's report since 1964 has emphasized that the single most significant source of preventable morbidity and premature mortality is cigarette smoking. The excess annual toll is estimated to exceed 350,000 people, more than all American lives lost in all wars during the twentieth century. Environmental pollution, crime and homicide, auto and home accidents, and poor nutrition are all significant sources of preventable morbidity and premature death, but smoking is considered the most significant.

449. The answer is C. *(Roemer, pp 49, 343-355.)* The volume of ambulatory medical visits compared with hospital admissions is very large indeed. Since 1931, the national average for physician visits per person per year has increased from 2.6 to 4.8 visits in 1978. Based on the total size of our population, this amounts to more than 1 billion visits per year. After World War II, the volume of outpatient visits to the general community hospital began to grow quite dramatically. Between 1965 and 1977, the number of outpatient visits to hospitals increased from 126 million to 264 million per year (a 209 percent increase). The numbers of inpatient admissions for those same years are 29 million and 37 million (a 27 percent increase). The doctor's office still represents the most likely setting for ambulatory medical services (68 percent). The hospital outpatient department represents 13 percent. Females average more visits per person per year than do males (5.4 to 4.0). Older people have more visits than do younger persons. By the age of 75, both males and females average about 6.4 visits per person to a physician. Respiratory diseases are the most frequent diagnostic category for visits to a physician's office (14.1 percent). Disturbances of the circulatory system represent the second rank in frequency (9.9 percent) followed by nervous system and sense-organ disorders. Fifty years ago, families with the highest income also had the greatest frequency of physician visits per year, but by 1977 the poorest families had more physician visits per person per year than did families with the highest incomes. The most likely explanation is the enactment of the Medicaid and Medicare laws in 1965, which financed medical services for the poor and the aged.

450. The answer is E. *(Last, ed 12. pp 1639-1650, 1770-1744.)* Health care costs in the United States are increasing at an alarming rate, with health expenditures representing an increasingly larger portion of family and governmental budgets. Current health expenditures by the federal government represent 13 percent of the total federal budget, with the federal budget contributing 40 percent of the funds for all health costs. Between 1940 and 1982 the percentage of GNP spent on health care more than doubled from 4.1 to 10.5 percent. Per capita expenditures for health care increased from $78 in 1950 to $1365 in 1980. The causes of the rise in health care costs are multiple. The general societal process of inflation has contributed to this to a great extent, along with the dramatic shift in the federal government's role of providing third-party payment for significant segments of the population, the increase in technology, and subspecialization. As these costs increase without apparent limit, legislators and other public officials are looking increasingly to prevention, in general, and life-style change, in particular, to bring these cost increases under control.

451. The answer is E. *(Rosen, pp 239-247.)* Recent analyses of the economic benefits of most health promotion programs in the work place show benefits in such areas as savings through smoking-cessation programs, less worker absenteeism, improved worker attitude and morale, decreased life and disability insurance costs, less use of medical care services, and increased recruitment value. All of these savings, however, appear to be overshadowed by the increased costs and demands on the company's pension fund. In effect, the prevention programs would prolong the lives of former workers in their economically nonproductive years. The question being debated by employers now is who will pay for the longer and better lives of the workers.

452. The answer is E. *(Last, ed 12. pp 1053-1056.)* The highest median per capita alcohol consumption by regions is in Australia and New Zealand, North America, and Europe. They are the most economically developed, share similar cultural heritages, and have a long history of acceptance and use of alcohol. France has the highest per capita consumption of alcohol (17.3 L) and Spain is eighth with 12.8 L per capita. Of the top 100 countries, the U.S. ranks thirtieth with 8.1 L per capita per year, Finland thirty-sixth with 6.9 L, and the U.S.S.R. fiftieth with 5.2 L per capita. Other countries with the highest per capita consumption include Barbados (16.2 L), Luxembourg (14.4 L), and Argentina and Portugal with 14.0 L per capita. In the past 10 years, France has shown a 14 percent decrease in per capita consumption and seven other countries have shown a small decrease. This has been attributed to changes in some consuming populations, economic trends, recent efforts of governments to deal with alcohol problems, and an increased awareness of health-related risks.

453. The answer is C. *(Last, ed 12. pp 1053-1057.)* Since World War II, there has been a general trend of increased production and consumption of alcohol. Major per capita consumption increases have been recorded in Europe, North America, Australia, and New Zealand. The countries with the greatest per capita increases between 1950 and 1980 were the German Democratic Republic (708 percent), the Federal German Republic (338 percent), the Netherlands (319 percent), Finland (276 percent), and Poland (190 percent). Other countries with over a 100 percent increase were Denmark, Hungary, Czechoslovakia, Ireland, Austria, and Norway. The U.S. has shown a 74 percent increase while France has shown a 14 percent decrease. Of interest is that each of the top eight countries showing the greatest increase has increased at a faster rate each decade, while France, Austria, Portugal, Yugoslavia, Ireland, and Britain have experienced a slight decrease, especially since 1976. The World Health Organization has expressed concern that the conduct of international trade and marketing in alcoholic beverages constitutes a serious international public health problem.

454. The answer is A. *(Raffel, ed 2. pp 1-16.)* Today's physician receives vastly different training from the practitioner in eighteenth- or nineteenth-century America. Today's medical practitioner has pursued a rigorous course of study in clinical practice under the close supervision of faculty who are typically at the forefront of the field of academic medicine. In colonial America, there were very few physicians. The first medical school was established in 1756 at the College of Philadelphia (later, University of Pennsylvania). The second school was founded at King's College (later, Columbia University) in 1768. At the time of the Revolutionary War, there were estimated to be 3,500 practitioners in the colonies of which only 400 had received any formal training. Apprenticeship to a practicing physician was the most common approach to training for a long period of time. The American Medical Association was founded in 1847 with the reform of medical education as a primary goal. In 1876, 22 medical schools organized the Association of American Medical Colleges as part of an effort to improve the quality of medical education. Beginning in 1902, *JAMA* published medical school failure statistics on state board licensing examinations, a form of exposure that could not help but embarrass and lead to institutional reform. In 1905, only five schools required any college preparation for admission. Ten years later, 85 schools prescribed a minimum of 1 or 2 years of college preparation. By 1932, every recognized medical school and most of the state licensing boards required at least 2 years of college work. Many required 3 years, and several required a college degree.

455. The answer is C. *(U.S. Public Health Service, 87-1232. pp 2, 167.)* The number and the percentage of women in the health professions have continued to increase significantly over the past 15 years. Between 1971–72 and 1984–85, the greatest increase occurred in dentistry—1.4 to 23.8 percent. The next greatest increase was in optometry (3.6 to 28.4 percent), followed by veterinary medicine (11.5 to 48.9 percent). Medicine has had an increase since 1971–72 from 10.9 to 31.7 percent. Pharmacology has more than doubled from 24.0 to 54.5 percent women and, except for nursing, has the highest percentage of women of all health profession schools.

456. The answer is C. *(Raffel, ed 2. pp 27-42.)* Specialization within the field of medicine began in the early 1900s and has continued down to the present time. The first specialty board to be incorporated was the American Board for Ophthalmic Examination in 1917. This group was renamed in 1933 as the American Board of Ophthalmology. The second specialty board, the American Board of Otolaryngology, was established in 1924. When the Advisory Board for Medical Specialties was established in 1933, there were only four existing certifying boards: obstetrics/gynecology, ophthalmology, otolaryngology, and dermatology/syphilology (later renamed dermatology). During the 1930s, a total of 13 specialty boards was established, covering the fields of obstetrics, dermatology, pediatrics, radiology, psychiatry, orthopedic surgery, colon and rectal surgery, urology, pathology, internal medicine, anesthesiology, plastic surgery, and surgery. In 1969, the American Board of Family Practice was established. In 1973, only 46 percent of the physicians practicing in the United States were diplomates of one or more of the 22 specialty boards. The Advisory Board of Medical Specialties became the American Board of Medical Specialties in 1970 and developed a close working relationship with the American Hospital Association, the Association of American Medical Colleges, the Federation of State Medical Boards, and the National Board of Medical Examiners. A fifth associate member joined in 1973, the Council of Medical Specialty Societies.

457. The answer is D. *(Williams, SJ, ed 2. pp 49-63.)* Utilization of health care services has shown some significant changes in the last 20 years. The differential in the utilization of health care services between the white and black populations has narrowed considerably. The percentages of whites and blacks seeing a physician in a 12-month period as reported in 1976 were nearly equivalent. This represented a shift of 20 percent from 1963, when the black population had a lower contact rate with physicians. Overall, there is a steady increase in the percentage of the population seeing a physician in any given year. Visits for diagnosis and treatment, compared with visits for preventive care, show a strong correlation with income level. For families earning $3000 per year, the numbers of visits for these two categories of care are nearly equal. For families earning $15,000 or more, the fraction of preventive visits is twice as large as that for diagnosis and treatment. This was based on data collected in 1971, but similar differentials continued throughout the 1970s. Males and females visit community mental health centers for outpatient care at nearly equal rates. Data collected on hospital inpatient utilization show that hospital admission rates have an inverse correlation with family income level. In general, hospital admissions rates have been increasing over time for older age categories, for lower income families, and for whites, while length of stay has been decreasing.

458. The answer is B. *(Andres, pp 53-80.)* The elderly utilize a disproportionate amount of health care resources. With the estimated increase in the 65-and-over age group from 24 million (11 percent) to 38 million (14 percent), there will be an increased demand for health care services between now and the year 2000. Also, with the shift of health problems from acute illness to more chronic and debilitating conditions, there will be additional need to increase continuing and long-term health care. Health care utilization data show women to be heavier users of services than men. With the increase in the elderly and with the female population progressively outnumbering the male population, the need for health care and help with social and economic problems in elderly females is expected to increase. The greater part of the sex differential in human longevity is considered to be the cumulative result of excessive male mortality throughout the life-span. This is because of increased risk behaviors and habits that increase the vulnerability of males to health problems. The decline in mortality of the elderly over the past 15 years is partly due to the reduction in mortality from cardiovascular disease, improvements in medical science, and a shift in the population toward more information and concern with their own health behaviors.

459. The answer is D. *(Williams, SJ, ed 2. pp 216-226.)* Nursing homes in the United States provide supervised care for medical and medically related problems. The term nursing home embraces those facilities that offer skilled nursing care, those that are personal care homes, and those with intermediate levels of care. The level of care is usually defined by the level of nursing effort required. The residents of nursing homes are most easily categorized by their age. The average age of the residents is 80 or more. Only 14.7 percent of the residents are under 65 years of age. Female residents outnumber male residents by a ratio of approximately 74 percent to 26 percent. In terms of marital status widowed persons (69 percent) outnumber never-married persons (14 percent). Married persons represent 12 percent of the resident population, and divorced or separated represent 4 percent. About 40 percent of patients enter the nursing home directly from their own residences. Another 35 percent are transferred from general hospitals, but this percentage is increasing. The rest come primarily from other institutions such as mental hospitals or long-term care specialty hospitals, other nursing homes, or boarding homes. The nursing home tends to collect the chronically ill. Patients frequently suffer from more than one illness or infirmity. The chronic conditions and impairments of nursing home residents are calculated in terms of prevalence per 1,000 residents. The most frequent conditions are senility (583.0), arthritis or rheumatism (342.5), heart trouble (335.1), mental illness (186.3), amputation of extremities (139.4), diabetes (132.6), paralysis (113.5), and glaucoma or cataracts (103.1). The prevalence of chronic impairments is accompanied by functional limitations. Thirty-two percent of the residents cannot hear a telephone conversation, 46 percent cannot read ordinary newsprint, 28 percent have lost bowel and bladder control, 51 percent have problems with mobility, and 31 percent are either chair-bound or bedridden. Other studies show that there are at least four disabled persons in the community for every three in a nursing home.

460. The answer is A. *(Matarazzo, pp 862-863.)* About 900,000 Americans die annually from cardiovascular diseases, about 700,000 from heart attack and 200,000 from stroke. This accounts for more than half of the deaths each year, and another million people become disabled each year by cardiovascular disease. In 1977, the cost was about 80 billion dollars (about 54 billion dollars in indirect costs and 26 billion dollars in direct medical care spending), which has increased tremendously over the past 10 years. This was 10 percent of the nation's medical costs. Hypertension is a major risk factor, increasing risk threefold for developing heart disease, sixfold for congestive heart failure, and sevenfold for stroke, yet hypertension can be effectively treated through pharmacological and behavioral interventions.

461. The answer is E (all). *(Roemer, pp 344-346.)* In 1978, the average number of ambulatory visits for the total population under 17 years of age was 4.1 per year. This increased steadily for all age groups to a high of 6.4 per year for people 75 and over. Urban areas, where more ambulatory services are available and are more accessible by public transportation, have a higher average number of ambulatory visits per individual than do rural areas. Members of the lowest income group make the most ambulatory care visits. However, visits to specialists are more prevalent among higher income groups. The lowest income group reports an average of three times as many days of sickness per year as does the highest income group.

462. The answer is B (1, 3). *(U.S. Public Health Service, 87-1232. pp 1, 85, 94.)* Infant mortality in the U.S. is now about one-third the rate it was in 1950 (29.2 per 1,000 births in 1950 versus 10.8 in 1984). Infant mortality for both black and white births in the U.S. has decreased at about the same rate since 1950, but black infant mortality remains about twice as high as that for white infants. Internationally, the U.S. ranks sixteenth among all countries, with Finland having the lowest infant mortality of all countries (6.5 deaths per 1,000 births). Finland is followed by Japan, Sweden, Switzerland, Norway, Denmark, France, and Canada (eighth). Availability and quality of prenatal and neonatal care are obviously major factors.

463. The answer is C (2, 4). *(U.S. Public Health Service, 87-1232. pp 1, 77.)* The number of pregnant women who do not receive prenatal care in the first trimester remains a problem. Since 1970, the percentage of mothers who received first trimester prenatal care increased from 68 percent in 1970 to 76.3 percent in 1980 and 76.5 percent in 1984. That was a 12 percent increase from 1970 to 1980, but since 1980 the percentage receiving prenatal care has remained about the same. Comparing white mothers with black mothers, from 1970 to 1980 black mothers achieved a 41 percent gain (44.4 to 62.7 percent) compared with a 10 percent gain for white mothers (72.4 to 79.3 percent). However, this increase has not continued since 1980, as both white and black prenatal care has remained the same. From 1980 to 1984, white mothers showed a bare increase from 79.3 to 79.6 percent, while black mothers showed a minimal decline from 62.7 to 62.2 percent.

464. The answer is B (1, 3). *(Last, ed 12. pp 1376-1380.)* Deinstitutionalization is a term used to describe the continuous decline in numbers of patients in state mental hospitals. It began about 1955 partly as the result of improved drug treatment programs. Policy and legislative changes 10 years later resulted in geographical decentralization and removed much of the power for involuntary commitments away from the mental hospitals (patients the hospitals had to accept). Thus, the state hospitals, which had provided a last resort for one class of society's rejected population (the chronically mentally ill), reduced their census and transferred much of the financial responsibility to the social welfare system, which has become increasingly fragmented with multiple disciplines and uncoordinated care. While the public investment in mental health and mental hospitals is higher than ever, the local, state, and federal agencies have been unable to take responsibility for the comprehensive psychiatric and social services needed by the chronically mentally ill.

465. **The answer is E (all).** *(Twaddle, ed 2. p 152.)* Native-American health care systems have contributed more to Western scientific medicine than any other cultural healing art. The ethnocentricity of Euro-Americans with respect to medicine has prevented our recognition and appreciation of this contribution. In so doing, we have ignored a large and important part of our cultural heritage. Native-American tribes discovered cures for scurvy, oral contraception, the use of antibiotics, and more than 200 drugs that are now officially listed in the *United States Pharmacopeia* since its first edition in 1920. It is not generally realized that knowledge and other benefits did not flow exclusively from our scientific Western culture into the so-called lower cultures of Native-American civilizations. In fact, the advice of Native-American healers was much sought after by white patients and physicians alike.

466. **The answer is E (all).** *(Williams, SJ, ed 2. pp 153-156.)* Physicians affiliated with health maintenance organizations have a strong financial incentive to provide medical care to enrolled members in a manner that emphasizes efficiency and economy. Prepayment for maintenance of health dictates minimal expenditures for patient care in order to maximize income. Means of accomplishing this include reducing the time patients spend in the hospital, doing as much diagnosis and therapy as possible on an outpatient basis, detecting disease early, and emphasizing preventive services.

467. **The answer is A (1, 2, 3).** *(Williams, SJ, ed 2. pp 196-208.)* The massive infusion of funds received by the health care system with the advent of Medicare and Medicaid in 1966 is directly associated with the substantial inflationary increase in individual health care costs. Additionally, labor costs account for as much as 70 percent of hospital budgets. The unionization of hospital employees and the resultant wage rise to industrial levels, coupled with the maintenance of separate staffs to handle underutilized maternity and newborn units, have contributed significantly to increased health care costs. Physicians' fees also have increased, but usually they are not part of a hospital bill.

468. **The answer is E (all).** *(Last, ed 12. p 1652.)* Group medical practice, a concept that is almost a century old, offers substantial benefits over solo practice to both physicians and their patients. Physicians benefit from a higher average income, a stimulating professional environment, and a structured work week. Some freedom of action is sacrificed, however. Patients benefit from specialized medical resources that are centralized in an atmosphere of cooperative teamwork in which greater attention can be paid to prevention and early diagnosis.

469. **The answer is A (1, 2, 3).** *(Andres, pp 53-71.)* The elderly, with more chronic illnesses and greater concern with decreasing health and function, will consume more and more of the health care resources as they increase in number and proportion of the population. Also, the decreasing number of aging males per aging females and the propensity of females to have a higher utilization rate of health services will add further to the demand for health services, particularly for older women. It is also expected that the improved educational and income levels of the elderly will increase the demand for and ability to afford health care. Interstate migration rates tend to be low among the elderly; that is, the elderly tend to remain in their own geographic area. Less than a third of the elderly live in central city areas, less than a third outside of central city areas, and more than a third live in nonmetropolitan areas where the elderly population growth is greatest. Thus, health care needs are also expected to increase in nonmetropolitan areas.

470. **The answer is A (1, 2, 3).** *(Williams, SJ, ed 2. pp 328-333.)* In 1978 there were more than 5 million people employed in health-related occupations. One-half of these were in nursing or related services, and they constitute the largest single group of health professionals in the country. Nursing remains a largely hospital-based profession. Nearly 75 percent of all nurses employed work in hospitals and nursing homes, and only 13 percent work in private physicians' offices and similar work places. The number of registered nurses in practice has grown since 1977, when it was 978,000, to 1,235,000 in 1980. The number of licensed practical nurses has shown a similar growth. Many hospitals report very high turnover rates in their nursing staffs. A rate of 50 percent turnover in a year is not unusual for many community and teaching hospitals in the United States. With almost one and a quarter million registered nurses in the United States, less than half of the employable nurses are working full-time. Increased demand will come from acute-care hospitals, long-term care, home-based care, and preventive care.

471. **The answer is A (1, 2, 3).** *(Andres, pp 959-960.)* The hospice movement is an attempt to provide care for the dying person resting along the journey of life toward death. It deals with some of the major patient, family, and health care provider conflicts encountered when patients are dying. The basic principles of the movement are self-determination, acceptance of death as a logical part of life, and the importance of family support. These are accomplished through providing in-patient, out-patient, and home services under the direction of the primary care physicians; utilizing the health care team concept; providing most primary care roles through family, hospice staff, and volunteers; early control of symptoms through aggressive and innovative approaches to pain, fear, and stress; pre-death and follow-up bereavement care for family; and support care for the staff and care-givers. Most often the patient is kept at home and as comfortable as possible until death.

472-475. **The answers are: 472-D, 473-A, 474-B, 475-D.** *(Williams, SJ, ed 2. pp 145-165.)* Health maintenance organizations deliver comprehensive medical care to voluntarily enrolled members through salaried physicians. The prepayment scheme encourages the practitioner to control costs of health care by affording providers the financial benefit that flows from keeping down the costs of patient care. A primary cost saving is through reduced hospitalization. The number of HMOs has grown from 50 in 1970 to more than 200 in 1980.

Group practice arrangements frequently provide for salaries for physician members who share resources in order to minimize costs. Prepayment by patients is rare. The cost for group practice services is no less, and sometimes higher, than for those services offered by solo private practitioners, as most physicians are specialists and use a fee-for-service payment scheme.

Many health agencies are proud of the comprehensiveness of their approach to health care, but most have areas of special interest. Thus, hospitals emphasize specialty care for seriously ill patients, although the trend has been to provide an increasing range of community health services. Community mental health centers, promulgated in 1963 by the Kennedy administration, have made psychiatric and psychological care available to a population that had once been consigned to ignorance and neglect. Such centers attempt to integrate a program that combines prevention, treatment, and rehabilitation.

Local health departments emphasize disease prevention measures such as community sewage and pollution control. Dissemination of medical information in the community, chronic disease control, and provision for home care of chronically ill persons all represent functions of a local health agency. Certain such services receive financial aid from state governments. Immunization services are also available.

476-479. The answers are: 476-A, 477-D, 478-C, 479-E. *(Williams, SJ, ed 2. pp 355-367.)* Medicare has two basic components. Part A is a compulsory hospital insurance plan for persons 65 years or older who are entitled to benefits under the Social Security or Railroad Retirement Acts. Social Security payroll taxes provide the funds for inpatient diagnostic studies, hospital room and board costs, and home care and extended care services. Part B is a voluntary supplementary insurance program that pays for outpatient visits, diagnostic studies, doctors' fees, home health services, and certain medical equipment. Costs are shared between the individual and the Federal General Revenue Fund, except for a deductible charge and 20 percent of physicians' fees.

Blue Cross is a prepaid, limited nonprofit commercial medical insurance plan to cover hospital costs. It has grown rapidly with the burgeoning costs of hospital care. It also has become increasingly popular as a negotiated health care benefit between industry and labor.

Blue Shield is the same kind of payment mechanism as Blue Cross, extended to cover physicians' fees in hospitals as well as surgery and emergency care. Blue Cross, Blue Shield, Medicare, and Medicaid reimburse physicians and hospitals on a "reasonable cost" basis, which has continued to increase dramatically.

The federal and state governments share the costs of Medicaid, although the program is administered by the states. The program provides medical care for low-income people of all ages and complements some of the provisions of Medicare. Medicare and Medicaid are providing limited and decreasing care. In spite of the four major payment plans discussed above, the major problems of equity, effectiveness, and economy still exist and are worsening. A very large segment of the population has no medical insurance coverage.

480-482. The answers are: 480-C, 481-C, 482-D. *(Rosen, pp 390-399.)* Social Security disability awards are highest for musculoskeletal (back pain) and mental disorders with back pain disabilities increasing at a rate more than ten times the growth of our population. The greatest number of Social Security disability awards for women are for mental disorders. The greatest number of awards for men and women combined are also for mental disorders. Of the various kinds of disability, back pain and mental disorders are most affected by the external contingencies of eligibility for WRF, duration of benefits, and percentage of WRF. These contingencies all influence the persistence of disability.

483-486. The answers are: 483-B, 484-C, 485-A, 486-D. *(U.S. Public Health Service, 87–1232. p 99.)* Heart disease is still the leading cause of death in the U.S. It reached a peak before 1950, but has continued to decline since then. Between 1970 and 1984 the death rate for heart disease decreased by 28 percent (from 253.6 to 183.6 deaths per 100,000 population). The rate for white males decreased 28 percent. The rates for both white and black females decreased 26 percent, but that for black males decreased only 20 percent.

Malignant neoplasms increased 3 percent between 1970 and 1984, from 129.9 per 100,000 population in 1970 to 133.5 in 1984. Lung cancer declined for white males, a development attributed to a decreasing prevalence of cigarette smoking, but this was accompanied by a sharp increase in lung cancer for women. In 1986, the incidence of lung cancer in women exceeded the incidence of breast cancer (formerly the highest form of cancer in women), and the former is expected to continue to increase over the next decade because of the increased smoking behavior of women.

Mortality from chronic obstructive pulmonary disease has increased by 34 percent (from 13.2 to 17.7 deaths per 100,000 population). This has primarily resulted from smoking behaviors. It has now become the fifth leading cause of death in the U.S., and it is increasing most rapidly in women.

Mortality from cerebrovascular diseases declined by 50 percent between 1970 and 1984. It is still the third or fourth leading cause of death in the U.S. The present rate is 33.4 deaths per 100,000 population. The annual rate of decrease has been about 5 percent per year since 1970 for both sexes and major race groups. Better control of hypertension and healthier cardiovascular systems are given as explanations.

The suicide rate has held rather constant with 9.1 deaths per 100,000 population in 1970 and 8.4 in 1984, although it has varied within subgroups such as adolescents and the elderly.

Biomedical and Behavioral Statistics

DIRECTIONS: Each question below contains five suggested responses. Select the **one best** response to each question.

487. All the following statements about nonparametric, distribution-free procedures are true EXCEPT that

(A) they test the hypothesis that two or more population distributions are identical
(B) they are preferable to parametric tests when samples are smaller than twelve
(C) the underlying population must be normally distributed
(D) variables can be measured with less than interval-level scales
(E) sample varieties may not be discontinuous

488. Two drugs were administered in several different doses, and the effects were measured and recorded. The data were subjected to regression and correlation analyses. The computed regression lines and correlation coefficients are presented below. Which of the following statements is true?

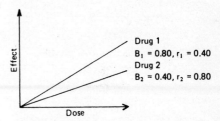

(A) In general, the strength of the causal relationship between two variables is indicated by the square of the correlation coefficient
(B) The proportion of variation in response to Drug 1 accounted for by dose is $(0.80)^2$
(C) The data indicate Drug 1 is more effective or powerful than Drug 2
(D) The data indicate Drug 1 is more potent than Drug 2
(E) There is more variability in responses to Drug 1 than to Drug 2

489. Two sedative-hypnotic drugs are being compared for relative efficacy in promoting sleep and also for possible differences in their effects on men and women. The results of a two-way analysis of variance are presented below. Of the following figures, which is the most plausible graphic representation of the observed effects?

Source of Variation	Sum of Squares	df	Mean Square	F	Significance
Drug	571.2	1	571.2	17.2	$p<0.01$
Sex	340.9	1	340.9	10.3	$p<0.01$
Drug x sex	63.3	1	63.3	1.9	NS
Residual	531.2	16	33.2		
Total	1506.4	19			

490. A sample of a population selected so that each observation or unit
has an equal chance of being included
is called a

(A) random population parameter
(B) systematic sample
(C) systematic random sample
(D) selected sample
(E) simple random sample

DIRECTIONS: Each question below contains four suggested responses of which **one or more** is correct. Select

A	if	**1, 2, and 3**	are correct
B	if	**1 and 3**	are correct
C	if	**2 and 4**	are correct
D	if	**4**	is correct
E	if	**1, 2, 3, and 4**	are correct

491. Many tests for statistical significance involve the F distribution. True statements about such tests include that

(1) the underlying populations must be normally distributed

(2) the numerator and denominator of the F ratio must be independent

(3) nominal-level data are **not** appropriate for dependent variables

(4) they test hypotheses about the shape of the underlying population distribution

492. The correlation coefficient is an important statistic in biomedical and behavioral research because

(1) the relationship between variables does not have to be linear

(2) it allows one to make valid inferences beyond the range of actual observation on which the analysis is based

(3) it is one of the most valid measures of causation

(4) it allows one to determine a measure of the degree or strength of the association between two variables

DIRECTIONS: Each group of questions below consists of lettered headings followed by a set of numbered items. For each numbered item select the **one** lettered heading with which it is **most** closely associated. Each lettered heading may be used **once, more than once, or not at all.**

Questions 493-496

For each experimental design, select the term with which it is most closely associated.

   (A) Randomized block design
   (B) Completely randomized design
   (C) Completely randomized factorial design
   (D) Split-plot or repeated measures design
   (E) Latin square design

493.

treatments

T_1	T_2	T_3	
P_{11}	P_{12}	P_{13}	
P_{21}	P_{22}	P_{23}	
P_{31}	P_{32}	P_{33}	15 patients, randomly assigned
P_{41}	P_{42}	P_{43}	to T_1, T_2, or T_3
P_{51}	P_{52}	P_{53}	
$\bar{P}_{.1}$	$\bar{P}_{.2}$	$\bar{P}_{.3}$	= treatment means

(P_{21} = patient 2, treatment 1)

494.

	treatments			
	T_1	T_2	T_3	ward means
ward 1	P_{11}	P_{12}	P_{13}	$\bar{P}_1.$
ward 2	P_{21}	P_{22}	P_{23}	$\bar{P}_2.$
ward 3	P_{31}	P_{32}	P_{33}	$\bar{P}_3.$
ward 4	P_{41}	P_{42}	P_{43}	$\bar{P}_4.$
ward 5	P_{51}	P_{52}	P_{53}	$\bar{P}_5.$
treatment means	$\bar{P}_{.1}$	$\bar{P}_{.2}$	$\bar{P}_{.3}$	$P_{..}$ = grand mean

3 patients from each of 5 wards, randomly assigned to T_1, T_2, or T_3

(P_{21} = patient from ward 2 in treatment 1)

495.

E

		age groups		
		20-40	41-60	61-80	weight means
weight groups	weight <120	P_{112}	P_{121}	P_{133}	$\bar{P}_{1..}$
	121-190	P_{213}	P_{222}	P_{231}	$\bar{P}_{2..}$
	>191	P_{311}	P_{323}	P_{332}	$\bar{P}_{3..}$
	age means	$\bar{P}_{.1.}$	$\bar{P}_{.2.}$	$\bar{P}_{.3.}$	grand mean = $\bar{P}_{...}$

9 patients, each categorized according to 2 nuisance variables, with treatment T_1, T_2, or T_3 assigned and specified by the 3rd subscript

treatment means
$T_1 = (P_{121} + P_{231} + P_{311})/3 = \bar{P}_{..1}$
$T_2 = (P_{112} + P_{222} + P_{332})/3 = \bar{P}_{..2}$
$T_3 = (P_{133} + P_{213} + P_{323})/3 = \bar{P}_{..3}$

(P_{213} = patient from weight group 2, age group 1, treatment 3)

496.

C

	treatment A			
	T_{A1}	T_{A2}	T_{A3}	treatment B means
T_{B1}	P_{111} P_{112} P_{113}	P_{121} P_{122} P_{123}	P_{131} P_{132} P_{133}	$\bar{P}_{1..}$
T_{B2}	P_{211} P_{212} P_{213}	P_{221} P_{222} P_{223}	P_{231} P_{232} P_{233}	$\bar{P}_{2..}$
T_{B3}	P_{311} P_{312} P_{313}	P_{321} P_{322} P_{323}	P_{331} P_{332} P_{333}	$\bar{P}_{3..}$
treatment A means	$\bar{P}_{.1.}$	$\bar{P}_{.2.}$	$\bar{P}_{.3.}$	$\bar{P}_{...}$ = grand mean

27 patients, randomly assigned to all combinations of 2 treatments, each with 3 levels

(P_{123} = treatment B1, treatment A2, patient 3)

Questions 497-500

For each outline of an experiment, select the form of statistical analysis that is most appropriate.

(A) Analysis of variance
(B) One-tail t-test
(C) Two-tail t-test
(D) Linear regression
(E) Chi-square

497. Does the inhibition of dopamine-sensitive adenylate cyclase have predictive value in assessing the potency of antipsychotic drugs? The data for each of 20 currently available antipsychotic drugs include an inhibition constant (K_i) that represents the drug concentration required to produce 50 percent inhibition of dopamine-stimulated cyclic AMP formation and an average clinical dose as a measure of potency

Drug	K_i (nM)	Approximate Equivalent Daily Dose (mg)
Chlorpromazine	50.0	100
Thioridazine	137.0	93
Fluphenazine	4.3	11
Trifluoperazine	18.0	6
.	.	.
.	.	.
.	.	.

498. Are black people who undergo a common surgical procedure more likely to be treated by a less experienced surgeon than are white people? The data represent hospital records from 340 patients undergoing gallbladder or hernia-repair operations in 10 randomly selected hospitals and include the patients' race (only black and white patients have been retained in the sample) and the status—resident or staff—of the surgeon

Race of Patient	Status of Surgeon Staff	Status of Surgeon Resident
Black	31	63
White	31	215

one tail t-test

B 499. Methylphenidate often is used in the management of a childhood syndrome known as hyperactivity or "minimal brain dysfunction." Does the drug also retard the growth of children? The data, taken from 15 children who have taken methylphenidate for at least 2 years and 15 unmedicated controls matched for age and sex, consist of each child's change in height over a 2-year period

Hyperactive, with Methylphenidate Δ Height (in)	Hyperactive, Unmedicated Δ Height (in)
3	5
7	4
4	8
5	2
•	•
• *19"*	• *9"*
•	•

500. Drug companies often claim that a particular aspirin preparation provides greater relief from arthritic pain than other apparently similar products. Are all aspirins alike? Two hundred subjects suffering from arthritis were randomly assigned to receive one of five aspirin preparations. The data are measures of increase in hand-gripping strength after treatment

Change in Hand-Gripping Strength (lb)
Treatment

1	2	3	4	5
10	8	4	3	6
8	2	9	2	2
3	4	4	5	8
7	9	7	5	7
•	•	•	•	•
•	•	•	•	•
•	•	•	•	•

analysis of variance

Biomedical and
Behavioral Statistics
Answers

487. The answer is C. *(Kirk, pp 491-493.)* Nonparametric procedures often are used when the more comprehens. e assumptions associated with parametric, or classic, procedures cannot be met. They require no assumptions about the shape of the population distribution and, in fact, are used to compare distributions rather than parameters estimated from distributions. Interval-level measurement is not required; many tests can be performed on nominal data. The only assumption associated with nonparametric tests, that of a variable with no discontinuities, is quite mild and is almost always met. Indeed, a nonparametric test is sometimes preferable even when the assumptions of parametric tests are met. Where small samples are involved, particularly less than six subjects per cell, nonparametric procedures have a smaller probability of type I and type II error than the corresponding parametric test.

488. The answer is E. *(Duncan, ed 2. pp 115-127.)* The only data available about the two drugs presented in the question are the regression coefficients (b) and the correlation coefficients (r) for a particular dosage range. Thus, one may conclude that the proportion of variation in responses to Drug 1 and Drug 2 accounted for by dose in that range is $r_1^2 = 0.16$ and $r_2^2 = 0.64$, respectively, or that there is more variability in response to Drug 1 than to Drug 2. There is no justification, however, for extrapolation in this context—the curves may even cross at higher doses. Finally, causal inferences from regression or correlation analyses are never justified.

489. The answer is B. *(Kirk, pp 177-178.)* The results in the analysis of variance table indicate that both main effects—drug and sex—were significant, but there was no interaction. Graphically, this means there should be two lines (one for men, one for women), the lines should not be horizontal (Drug A was different from Drug B), and the lines should be parallel (there was no interaction). Choice C is an example of a sex effect but no drug effect or interaction; choice A represents a drug effect with no sex effect and no interaction; and choices D and E both illustrate significant main effects **with** an interaction. Choice B is only one of several possible correct representations, however, because the data presented do not disclose which drug was the more effective or whether both drugs were more effective with men or with women. Thus, other plausible figures would include:

490. The answer is E. *(Duncan, ed 2. pp 54-55.)* When a mean and a standard deviation are calculated by using the data from the entire population, they are called population parameters. When they are calculated from a sample of that population they are referred to as sample statistics. In choosing a sample, the objective is to select observations or units that are truly representative of the total population being studied. If the sample is selected so that each observation or unit has an equal chance of being included in the sample, it is called a simple random sample. Randomness does not mean haphazardness, selecting something without intentional bias, having someone else choose, or using some general techniques, such as drawing from a hat, "randomly" pointing one's finger, or dart throwing. Using a table of random numbers or some mechanical means is considered best. An example of using a systematic sample would be interviewing every third person. Every possible source of sample bias must be explored.

491. The answer is A (1, 2, 3). *(Kirk, pp 42-43.)* Statistical tests that employ the *F* distribution as the theoretical model are called "parametric" tests because they compare parameters estimated from sample distributions rather than the distributions themselves. Consequently, most of the assumptions concerning their use—normally distributed populations, continuous variables, and equal population variances—act to preserve the accuracy of the estimation procedures. There is the additional restriction that the observations must be independent because the computed *F* test value is a ratio of explained to unexplained variance. Any correlation between the observations would make such a ratio meaningless.

492. The answer is D (4). *(Duncan, ed 2. pp 115-128.)* A correlation analysis is used to obtain a measure of the degree or strength of association between two variables under study. This degree of association between *X* and *Y* is provided by *r*, the coefficient of correlation. Although this is one of the most frequently used statistics, it is important to observe several precautions: (1) the relationship between variables must be linear, (2) there is a real danger of making inferences beyond the range of actual observations or measurements on which the analysis is based, and (3) it must always be remembered that correlation does not necessarily mean causation. A significant correlation is an indication that the two variables, *X* and *Y*, tend to be associated. The problem is that it is possible that a third variable may be affecting the relationship, thus causing both *X* and *Y* to vary together.

493-496. The answers are: 493-B, 494-A, 495-E, 496-C. *(Kirk, pp 11-20.)* Choosing the appropriate design for an experiment is crucial because the design involves a plan for assigning subjects to treatment groups, it expresses the relation being tested between the dependent and independent variables, and it organizes the effects of nuisance variables so that they can be tested and considered accordingly. The simplest experimental design is the completely randomized design. As the name implies, random assignment of subjects to treatments is essential if inferences drawn are to be logically valid. The hypothesis tested by this design—that all group means are equal—is evaluated with an F ratio.

The randomized block design, although very similar to the completely randomized design, tests the additional hypothesis that grouping the subjects according to one other variable, usually a background variable, will account for some variance previously left in the error term. This design and the others discussed below also employ an F ratio to test their hypotheses.

Subjects in a Latin square design are grouped according to two background or blocking variables in order to reduce further the error variance. If it can be assumed that there is no interaction between the two blocking variables, and if there are an equal number of treatment levels, rows, and columns, treatment levels can be randomly assigned to the cells such that each treatment occurs in each row and each column exactly once. The random assignment of treatment levels to cells reduces the sample size considerably from that which would be required if all treatment levels were given to all cells.

The completely randomized factorial essentially is a completely randomized design for two independent variables or factors. Again, all subjects must be randomly assigned to all cells. This design permits the simultaneous test of two main treatment effects as well as any interaction effect between the two treatments.

497-500. The answers are: 497-D, 498-E, 499-B, 500-A. *(Goldstein, pp 51-53, 63-64, 102-104, 129-131.)* The experiment in the first question is designed to investigate the possibility that a linear relationship exists between an inhibition constant and the potency of antipsychotic drugs. This is a curve-fitting (as opposed to a difference) hypothesis, and a parametric procedure is justified because the data are continuous, ratio-level variables (choice D).

The experiment in the second question compares a set of counts in a contingency table with the expected distribution, given the unequal proportions of black and white patients. This is not a two-way analysis of variance, however. The data in the four cells are not means of randomly sampled, ordinal-level, or better variables; they are counts of binary variables (in a cell or not in a cell). The chi-square test (choice E) is designed for such enumeration data, regardless of the number of categories or the sample size.

The experiment in the third question is a test for differences between two groups measured with continuous, ratio-level variables. A one-tail t-test (choice B) is the best choice because the experiment is not concerned with whether methylphenidate retarded or accelerated children's growth, just whether it retarded growth. Both the two-tail t-test and the analysis of variance are inappropriate because they test two-tailed hypotheses.

The experiment in the fourth question is similar to that in the third: both test for differences between groups measured with continuous, ratio-level variables. An analysis of variance (choice A) is the best choice here, however, because this experiment tests a two-tailed, not a one-tailed, hypothesis, and there are more than two groups to compare.

Bibliography

Ader R (ed): *Psychoneuroimmunology.* New York, Academic Press, 1981.

Allen RW, Porter LW: *Organizational Influence Processes.* Glenview, IL, Scott, Foresman, 1983.

Anastasi A: *Psychological Testing,* 5th ed. New York, Macmillan, 1982.

Andres R, Bierman EL, Hazzard WR: *Principles of Geriatric Medicine.* New York, McGraw-Hill, 1985.

Atchley RD: *Social Forces and Aging,* 4th ed. Belmont, CA, Wadsworth, 1985.

Baron RA, Byrne D: *Social Psychology: Understanding Human Interaction,* 4th ed. Boston, Allyn & Bacon, 1984.

Bell RR: *Marriage and Family Interaction,* 6th ed. Homewood, IL, Dorsey Press, 1983.

Botwinick J: *Aging and Behavior: A Comprehensive Integration of Research Findings.* 4th ed. New York, Springer Publishing, 1984.

Braunwald E, et al: *Harrison's Principles of Internal Medicine,* 11th ed. New York, McGraw-Hill, 1987.

Brenner C: *An Elementary Textbook of Psychoanalysis.* New York, Doubleday, 1974.

Brody JE: *Jane Brody's Nutrition Book,* 2nd ed. New York, Bantham, 1987.

Brophy JE, Willis SL: *Human Development and Behavior.* New York, St. Martin's Press, 1982.

Brown TS, Wallace PM: *Physiological Psychology.* New York, Academic Press, 1980.

Carlson NR: *Physiology of Behavior,* 3rd ed. Boston, Allyn & Bacon, 1986.

Carroll D: *Living with Dying.* New York, McGraw-Hill, 1985.

Conger JJ, Petersen AC: *Adolescence and Youth: Psychological Development in a Changing World,* 3rd ed. New York, Harper & Row, 1983.

Counte MA, Christman LP: *Interpersonal Behavior and Health Care.* Boulder, Westview Press, 1981.

Davison GC, Neale JM: *Abnormal Psychology: An Experimental-Clinical Approach,* 4th ed. New York, John Wiley & Sons, 1986.

Deci EL, Ryan RM: *Intrinsic Motivation and Self-Determination in Human Behavior*. New York, Plenum Publishing, 1985.

Doleys DM, Meredith RL, Ciminero AR (eds): *Behavioral Medicine: Assessment and Treatment Strategies*. New York, Plenum Publishing, 1982.

Duncan RD, Knapp RG, Miller MC: *Introductory Biostatistics for the Health Sciences*, 2nd ed. New York, John Wiley & Sons, 1983.

Ebersole P, Hess P: *Toward Healthy Aging: Human Needs and Nursing Response*, 2nd ed. St. Louis, CV Mosby, 1985.

Eiser JR (ed): *Social Psychology and Behavioral Medicine*. New York, John Wiley & Sons, 1982.

Erikson EH: *Identity: Youth and Crisis*. New York, WW Norton, 1968.

Eysenck HJ: *Personality, Genetics, and Behavior: Selected Papers*. New York, Praeger, 1982.

Feuerstein M, Labbe EE, Kuczmierczyk AR: *Health Psychology*. New York, Plenum Press, 1986.

Freeman HE, et al: *Handbook of Medical Sociology*, 3rd ed. Englewood Cliffs, NJ, Prentice-Hall, 1979.

Froelich RD, Bishop FM: *Clinical Interviewing Skills*, 3rd ed. St. Louis, CV Mosby, 1977.

Goldstein A: *Biostatistics: An Introductory Text*. New York, Macmillan, 1964.

Grant M: *Handbook of Community Health*, 3rd ed. Philadelphia, Lea & Febiger, 1981.

Guthrie HA: *Introductory Nutrition*, 6th ed. St. Louis, CV Mosby, 1986.

Hall CS, Lindzey G: *Theories of Personality*, 3rd ed. New York, John Wiley & Sons, 1978.

Hall JF: *Classical Conditioning and Instrumental Learning: A Contemporary Approach*. Philadelphia, JB Lippincott, 1976.

Hamburg DA, Elliott GR, Parron DL (eds): *Health and Behavior: Frontiers of Research in the Biobehavioral Sciences*. Washington, DC, National Academy Press, 1982.

Hollander EP, Hunt RG (eds): *Current Perspectives in Social Psychology*, 4th ed. New York, Oxford University Press, 1976.

Iversen SD, Iversen LL: *Behavioral Pharmacology*, 2nd ed. New York, Oxford University Press, 1981.

Jaco EG (ed): *Patients, Physicians, and Illness: A Sourcebook in Behavioral Science and Health*, 3rd ed. New York, Macmillan, 1979.

Kammeyer KCW: *Marriage and Family.* Boston, Allyn & Bacon, 1987.

Kandel ER, Schwartz JH (eds): *Principles of Neural Science,* 2nd ed. New York, Elsevier, 1985.

Kaplan HI, Sadock BJ: *Modern Synopsis of Comprehensive Textbook of Psychiatry,* vol 4, 4th ed. Baltimore, Williams & Wilkins, 1984.

Kirk RE: *Experimental Design: Procedures for the Behavioral Sciences.* Belmont, CA, Wadsworth Publishing, 1968.

Klaus MH, Kenell JH: *Parent-Infant Bonding,* 2nd ed. St. Louis, CV Mosby, 1982.

Kolb B, Whishaw IQ: *Human Neuropsychology,* 2nd ed. New York, WH Freeman, 1985.

Lanyon RI, Goodstein LD: *Personality Assessment,* 2nd ed. New York, John Wiley & Sons, 1982.

Last JM (ed): *Maxcy-Rosenau Public Health and Preventive Medicine,* 12th ed. Norwalk, CT, Appleton-Century-Crofts, 1986.

Leigh H, Reiser MF: *The Patient: Biological, Psychological, and Social Dimensions of Medical Practice,* 2nd ed. New York, Plenum Publishing, 1985.

Lerner RM, Galambos NL: *Experiencing Adolescence: A Sourcebook for Parents, Teachers, and Teens.* New York, Garland, 1984.

Lerner RM, Hultsch DE: *Human Development: A Life-Span Perspective.* New York, McGraw-Hill, 1983.

Lerner RM, et al: *Psychology.* New York, Macmillan, 1986.

Lindzey G, Aronson A (eds): *The Handbook of Social Psychology,* vol 2, 3rd ed. New York, Random House, 1985.

Madsen KB: *Theories of Motivation.* Kent, OH, Kent State University Press, 1968.

Matarazzo JD, Weiss SM, Herd JA, Miller NE (eds): *Behavioral Health: A Handbook of Health Enhancement and Disease Prevention.* New York, John Wiley & Sons, 1984.

Mechanic D: *Medical Sociology,* 2nd ed. New York, Macmillan, 1978.

Middlebrook PN: *Social Psychology & Modern Life,* 2nd ed. New York, Alfred A. Knopf, 1980.

Miller SA (ed): *Nutrition and Behavior.* Philadelphia, Franklin Institute Press, 1981.

Mischel W: *Introduction to Personality,* 4th ed. New York, Holt, Rinehart & Winston, 1986.

Mussen PH, Conger JJ, Kagan J, Huston AC: *Child Development and Personality,* 6th ed. New York, Harper & Row, 1984.

Ornstein R, Thompson RF: *The Amazing Brain.* Boston, Houghton Mifflin, 1984.

Plomin R, DeFries JJ, McClearn GE: *Behavioral Genetics: A Primer.* San Francisco, WH Freeman, 1980.

Raffel MW: *The U.S. Health System: Origins and Functions.* New York, John Wiley & Sons, 1980.

Roemer MI: *Ambulatory Health Services in America: Past, Present and Future.* Rockville, MD, Aspen Systems Corp., 1981.

Rosen JC, Soloman LJ (eds): *Prevention in Health Psychology.* Hanover, NH, University Press of New England, 1985.

Sarason IG, Sarason BR: *Abnormal Psychology: The Problem of Maladaptive Behavior,* 4th ed. Englewood Cliffs, NJ, Prentice-Hall, 1984.

Sears DO, Freedman JL, Peplau LA: *Social Psychology,* 5th ed. Englewood Cliffs, NJ, Prentice-Hall, 1985.

Schneiderman N, Tapp J: *Behavioral Medicines: The Biopsychosocial Approach,* Hillsdale, NJ, Lawrence Earlbaum Assoc., 1985.

Schuster CS, Ashburn SS: *The Process of Human Development: A Holistic Approach,* 2nd ed. Boston, Little, Brown, 1986.

Simons RC (ed): *Understanding Human Behavior in Health and Illness,* 3rd ed. Baltimore, Williams & Wilkens, 1985.

Steers RM, Porter LW: *Motivation and Work Behavior,* 3rd ed. New York, McGraw-Hill, 1983.

Steptoe A, Mathews A: *Health Care and Human Behavior.* New York, Academic Press, 1984.

Suinn RM: *Fundamentals of Abnormal Psychology.* Chicago, Nelson-Hall, 1984.

Thibaut JW, Kelley HH: *The Social Psychology of Groups.* New York, John Wiley & Sons, 1979.

Thompson RF: *Introduction to Physiological Psychology.* New York, Harper & Row, 1975.

Tryon WW (ed): *Behavioral Assessment in Behavioral Medicine.* New York, Springer, 1985.

Twaddle AC, Hessler RM: *A Sociology of Health,* 2nd ed. New York, Macmillan, 1986.

U.S. Public Health Service: *Health United States 1986,* PHS No. 87-1232. Hyattsville, MD, Department of Health, Education and Welfare, 1986.

Vander Zanden JW: *Social Psychology,* 4th ed. New York, Random House, 1987.

Weiss SM, Herd JA, Fox BH (eds): *Perspectives on Behavioral Medicine,* vol 1. New York, Academic Press, 1981.

Weiss SM, Matthews KA, Detre T, Graef JA (eds): *Stress, Reactivity and Cardiovascular Disease*, NIH No. 84-2698. Washington, D.C., U.S. Department of Health and Human Services, 1984.

Williams RB: *Perspectives on Behavioral Medicine: Neuroendocrine Control and Behavior*, vol 2. New York, Academic Press, 1985.

Williams SJ, Torrens PR: *Introduction to Health Services*, 2nd ed. New York, John Wiley & Sons, 1984.

Winefield HR, Peay MY: *Behavioral Science in Medicine*. London, Allen & Unwin, 1980.

Wrightsman LS: *Social Psychology*, 2nd ed. Monterey, CA, Brooks/Cole Publishing, 1978.

Appetite → Hypothalmus – ventromedial part

577-0447